Ashanti
Gold

Ashanti Gold

THE AFRICAN LEGACY OF THE WORLD'S
MOST PRECIOUS METAL

PROFESSOR EDWARD S. AYENSU

ASHANTI GOLDFIELDS

PROJECT EDITOR: Esther Labi

PUBLISHING CONSULTANT: Bruce Marshall

EDITOR: Anne Kilborn

ART DIRECTOR: Sean Keogh

DESIGNERS: Roger Fawcett-Tang, Colin Loughry

DTP EDITORS: Lesley Gilbert, Kate Waghorn

RESEARCH: James Rankin, Michaela Moher

PICTURE RESEARCH: Elaine Willis

PRODUCTION: Nikki Ingram

Ashanti Goldfields Company Limited
Registered Office: Gold House, Patrice Lumumba Road,
Roman Ridge, Accra, Ghana
Postal Address: P.O. Box 2665, Accra, Ghana

Conceived, edited and designed by
Marshall Editions
170 Piccadilly
London W1V 9DD

Originated in England by DP Graphics
Printed and bound in Italy

Contents

Foreword by His Excellency The President of the Republic of Ghana,
Flight Lieutenant Jerry John Rawlings

Introduction	Ashanti Goldfields Company	8
Chapter One	The Noble Metal	26
Chapter Two	Finding Gold	50
Chapter Three	The Gold Worker's Story	98
Chapter Four	The Spread of Gold	120
Chapter Five	Working with Gold	134
Chapter Six	The Value of Gold	182
Index		196

An Agreement made this _Third_ day

of June 1897 **Between** SIR WILLIAM EDWARD MAXWELL K.C.M.G. Governor and Commander-in-Chief of the GOLD COAST COLONY (hereinafter called "the Governor" which expression shall in this Agreement mean and include the Officer for the time being administering the Government of the said Colony) of the first part JOSEPH EDWARD BINEY JOSEPH ETTRUSON ELLIS and JOSEPH PETER BROWN all of Cape Coast in the said Colony Merchants of the second part and THE CÔTE D'OR COMPANY LIMITED having its Registered Offices at No. 38 Finsbury Pavement in the City of London of the third part and ASHANTI GOLDFIELDS CORPORATION LIMITED having its Registered Offices at No. 2 Aldermanbury Postern in the same City (hereinafter called "the Company" which expression shall in this Agreement where the context so admits include its successors and assigns) of the fourth part.

Whereas by an Indenture dated the 1st day of August 1895 and made between Yaw Boyakey then King of Bekwai of the one part and the said Joseph Edward Biney, Joseph Ettruson Ellis and Joseph Peter Brown of the other part an Indenture therein mentioned made by Quacoe Osai then late King of Bekwai and dated the 3rd day of March 1890 was expressed to be confirmed and modified and the land hereinafter described together with the mining and other liberties specified in the Indenture now in recital were expressed to be leased to the said Joseph Edward Biney, Joseph Ettruson Ellis and Joseph Peter Brown for a term of 99 years from the 3rd day of March 1890 at the yearly rent of £100 until the said premises should be sold or disposed of and after the lapse of one year from the time when the said premises should have been sold or disposed of at the yearly rent of £133.

And whereas by an Agreement dated the 15th day of August 1895 and made between Kwaku Nkansa then King of Adansi of the one part and the said Joseph Edward Biney, Joseph Ettruson Ellis and Joseph Peter Brown of the other part the said King of Adansi purported to confirm the hereinbefore recited Indenture subject to the payment of the yearly rent of £66 to the King of Adansi for the time being and the said Indentures of the 3rd day of March 1890 and the 1st day of August 1895 and the said Agreement of the 15th day of August 1895 are hereinafter collectively referred to as "the Concessions."

And whereas by an Agreement made the 27th day of August 1895 between the said Joseph Edward Biney, Joseph Ettruson Ellis and Joseph Peter Brown of the one part and the Côte d'Or Company Limited of the other part the premises comprised in the said Indenture of the 1st day of August 1895 and the said Agreement of the 15th day of August 1895 were agreed to be sold to the Côte d'Or Company Limited for the consideration therein mentioned and it was thereby agreed that such sale should be completed on the 1st day of May 1896.

Foreword

*By His Excellency The President of the Republic of Ghana,
Flight Lieutenant Jerry John Rawlings*

*As Ashanti Goldfields Company celebrates its one
hundredth anniversary, it gives me great pleasure to
contribute a Foreword to the book commemorating this
historic occasion.*

*It is noteworthy that the publication has been
specially dedicated to the celebration of the prominent role
gold has played in the culture and history of our people
throughout the ages.*

*From its inception, Ashanti Goldfields promised to
be a significant player in the economic life and
prosperity of our country. Endowed with legendary gold
deposits, its capacity to promote the economic
development of the country was shackled only by the
limitations of the political-administrative environment
in which it had been allowed to operate.*

*The economic changes of the early 1980s, which
culminated in the Economic Recovery Programme of
1983, and the policy measures that were instituted
specifically for the mining sector under the Ghana
Minerals Code of 1986 triggered phenomenal growth in
that sector. Ashanti typifies that remarkable surge.
Annually, the company produces more than one million
ounces of gold compared with 240,000 ounces before the
promulgation of the Minerals Code – with 850,000
ounces coming from its Obuasi operations alone.*

*The gold mining sector has now emerged as the
country's largest foreign-exchange earner, accounting
for more than 40 percent of the country's total gross
foreign-exchange earnings. Ashanti itself is now one of
the world's leading gold mining companies. Indeed, its
performance over the last decade should be an example
to other Ghanaian establishments. I am pleased that, in
recent years, many of our sister nations that are
endowed with gold reserves have invited Ashanti to
collaborate with them in the development and
management of their resources. I am delighted to learn
that Ashanti is presently managing more than 35
projects in as many as 14 African countries.*

*It is a source of
inspiration to the
present generation of
Ghanaians that the
foundation of this success
story was the initiative of
three Ghanaian entrepreneurs,
who acquired land rights to the original
Obuasi concessions in 1895. One hundred years later,
Africans are still at the helm of what is now an
international company. Today, Ashanti's affairs are
skilfully managed by a team made up predominantly of
Ghanaians and nationals from the other African
countries where it operates.*

*I have every hope that Ashanti will proceed
confidently into the next century, guided and inspired
by its own enviable record to reach toward greater
heights in the continent of its birth, and even beyond.*

*Ashanti Gold does not dwell exclusively on these
themes, for the book attempts to trace the salient role of
gold in Ghana's rich culture, against the backdrop of the
general sentiment that the metal evokes worldwide. But
it also draws attention to the contribution that AGC
itself has made to the generation of national wealth, as
well as the promotion of international prosperity.*

*For Africa, for Ghana and for Ashanti, this moment
is both an auspicious beginning and a culminating
achievement, as we watch one of Africa's true success
stories embark on its second century of commercial life.
On this occasion, therefore, I salute the workers,
management and directors of Ashanti Goldfields – both
past and present – on their contribution to the company's
achievements, the progress of our country, the
development of our continent and the advancement of
our world. That is the true value of Ashanti Gold.*

J. J. Rawlings.

ASHANTI
GOLDFIELDS COMPANY

Introduction

By the Chief Executive of Ashanti Goldfields Company Ltd, Sam E. Jonah

The publication of Ashanti Gold is momentous in many respects. It represents the first major attempt by an international company to capture, for posterity, the mystique surrounding the special place that history has preserved for gold in the African psyche. Secondly, the evolution of Ashanti Goldfields Company, the sponsors of this book, is itself embedded in the history of the development of gold in Ghana, a country whose rich gold reserves earned it the name the Gold Coast.

Over the centuries, people have come from far and wide to support an industry which in recent years has emerged as the highest foreign-exchange earning sector in our economy. But to the Ghanaian, gold will for ever remain virtually a sacred commodity, and in part Ashanti Gold seeks to celebrate the emotive influence that this regal metal continues to wield over millions of minds the world over.

In the famed Kingdom of Ashanti, gold played and continues to play many roles – political, ornamental and symbolic – exemplifying its special place in Ghanaian culture and tradition. Ashanti gold-weights are world renowned, but fewer people realize that before currencies were introduced, people of the Gold Coast used gold dust as a medium of exchange for goods and services.

Ashanti Goldfields is a product of Africa's long and diverse association with gold. It is for this reason that, after 100 years of operations, the Company has thought it fit to release this volume in 1997 to commemorate Africa's immense relationship with this noble metal. The year 1897 is notable for other reasons: Ashanti Goldfields Corporation was listed on the London Stock Exchange, a landmark for African commerce. From the start, AGC was a joint effort with the British to pool resources to develop what is now a legendary ore body – the Obuasi mine. This tradition of collaboration continues to inform the relationship between the Company and the investor community.

Ashanti's London listing in 1897 was the culmination of the pioneering work of Chief J.E. Biney, J.E. Ellis and J.P. Brown, three Ghanaian entrepreneurs who secured a mining concession in Obuasi in 1895. The remarkably high-grade rock samples that their efforts yielded, together with their association with British merchant Edwin Cade, drew international attention to the rich mineral endowment of this African nation.

One hundred years later, Ashanti still mines this venerable ore body in the area of the original concession. Furthermore, in the past three years the Company has emerged as a truly multinational African enterprise operating in no fewer than 14 African countries. Ashanti now operates four mines – Ayanfuri, Iduapriem and Obuasi in Ghana, and Freda Rebecca in Zimbabwe. It also has two new mines under construction – Bibiani in Ghana and Siguiri in Guinea. From its modest beginnings, Ashanti is now a public company listed on stock exchanges in six countries – Ghana, the United Kingdom, Zimbabwe, Australia, Canada and the United States, where Ashanti became the first African company to be listed on the New York Stock Exchange.

I take great pride in the fact that this publication coincides with Ghana's 40th Independence Anniversary. The new expansionary paradigm at Ashanti captures the spirit and epitomizes the dreams of Osagyefo Dr Kwame Nkrumah and other founding fathers of Africa, who showed remarkable foresight in setting the stage for the development of Africa's natural resources. I am especially grateful to President Rawlings for accepting the invitation to write the Foreword to this volume. It was Rawlings' Administration which, in 1986, introduced the changes in the Minerals and Mining Law which established an enabling environment for new investment, giving Ashanti the impetus to move forward. I am particularly grateful for his personal interest in Ashanti's well-being.

As we celebrate AGC's centenary, I would like to express my personal gratitude for the loyalty exhibited by the shareholders, the directors and the entire workforce – both past and present – to the Company's development. We will continue to focus on the corporate vision and mission which history, tradition and our own commitment to excellence have bestowed on us. This is the message that our involvement in the publication of Ashanti Gold seeks to convey to the world.

A century of continuity: the Ellis shaft, still AGC's main hoisting shaft, is on the site of the original Ellis Mine, named for one of the company's founders. It hauls ore and waste from underground workings in the northern part of the concession.

L ate in 1897, the principals of the newly formed Ashanti Goldfields Corporation led a team that dragged and carried 40 tonnes of equipment nearly 200 km (120 miles) from the coast to begin exploitation of their new property at Obuasi. On New Year's Eve they made their first mark on the land. It was the birth of an enterprise which, exactly 100 years on, is a flagship African company and Ghana's foremost earner of foreign exchange. Over the years, 25 million ounces of gold have derived from its efforts – $10 billion dollars' worth if it were all valued at today's price.

Gold has long been panned and mined from the quartz reefs of Ashanti by local goldseekers, the galamsey. But it was not until toward the end of the 19th century that the idea of an orderly commercial approach to gold mining in the Gold Coast began to gather momentum.

Europeans had rarely ventured peaceably into the region – the powerful Ashanti dynasty had terrorized intruders and dominated neighbours for centuries – but travellers knew of this "neglected Eldorado", as Sir Richard Burton called it. British soldiers returned from the Ashanti wars with nuggets of ore bearing glittering streaks of the precious metal. One intrepid traveller told the Liverpool Chamber of Commerce that he had passed through districts where "you could pick up gold as you would potatoes".

During the 1870s, a Frenchman, Marie Joseph Bonnat, signed leases and exploited concessions on the River Ankobra at Awuda and later at Tarkwa, but his rights died with him in 1882. Thus it was two Fante merchants from Cape Coast, Joseph E. Ellis and Chief Joseph E. Biney, and their accountant, Joseph P. Brown, who opened the modern story of Ashanti gold.

Lured by travellers' tales, they crossed the River Pra into the kingdom of Adansi and saw the outcrops being worked for the king of Bekwai by local prospectors. In March 1890, the partners negotiated the mining concessions for 25,900 hectares (100 sq miles) of land in the Obuasi District. Among the foothills of the Moinsi and Kwisa ranges, between the rivers Oda and Offin, they laid claim to what was, and still is, one of the world's richest goldfields.

THE ELLIS MINE

Naming his new property the Ellis Mine, Joseph Ellis abandoned the tributors' primitive practice of pitting down on outcrops which eventually became too deep and too dangerous to work. Instead he sank shafts on reef and laid out interconnecting tunnels. Stoping was limited to the richest seams showing visible gold. An experienced international trader and agent, he ordered mining equipment through the London firm of Smith and Cade, which was shortly to have a fateful impact on his endeavour. As well as essentials such as hammers, picks and shovels, he imported three hand-operated stamp mills and amalgam retorts. He also introduced the use of gunpowder for blasting and imported a gunpowder machine to grade and measure the charges for muzzle-loading guns and rock blasting.

Biney, Ellis and Brown formed a syndicate with the Mine Manager, J.P. Wilson. They ran the Ellis Mine for five years, but it must eventually have become apparent that the vast goldfield, stretching over several kilometres on the strike of the quartz reefs, required more expertise and capital and that the sale of the concession would be financially beneficial.

Biney had sent specimens of gold-bearing quartz to the London merchant who supplied his equipment. But little interest had been shown there until Edwin Arthur Cade joined the firm as a partner through marriage to one of Smith's daughters. When yet another batch of specimens arrived, this time with the urgent invitation to "come and see!" Cade had the sample assayed. The London assayers Johnson Matthey reported on 20 April 1895 that there was more than eight ounces of gold per ton of quartz.

Cade wasted little time in arranging to meet Biney and Ellis in Cape Coast. Only when he arrived did he realize that the gold-bearing area was not in the tranquil, accessible Cape Coast but in the remote and then hostile Ashanti region. "I am

determined, however, to proceed at all risks," he wrote, "and so to shape my course that even in the event of a purchase not being at present possible, the position of the company may still be a desirable one in the event of annexation [by Her Majesty's Government]."

CADE'S CONCESSION

In July 1895, Cade, Ellis and Biney, who had reached an agreement over the sale of the Ellis Mine, journeyed to Obuasi to obtain approval for their proposed transaction from the Chiefs of Bekwai and Adansi. On 16 August, the transfer of the concession to Cade was signed and sealed in the presence of the Chiefs and Elders at Bekwai. On their return to Cape Coast, the provisional agreement with the vendors (Biney and Ellis) and the specially set up Côte d'Or Mining Company was signed in Cape Coast Castle and dated 27 August 1895, with a £200 deposit from Cade.

He returned to London with his grants in his pocket, but it was to be another two years before he could begin to exploit his new acquisition. With the destoolment

Joseph P. Brown was the early administrator and accountant at Ellis Mine.

Just eight months after ground was first broken by AGC, the various parts of the mill, boiler house and engine parts were housed under these wooden structures, thus demonstrating considerable mining activity.

Blasting often exposes gold on the surface of lumps of quartz. More will be ground out as the ore is processed.

and deportation of the Ashanti King, Nana Prempeh I, in 1896, the Ashanti Protectorate was brought more directly under British control and Cade went to great lengths to ensure that the grant for the concession was ratified by the British Government. In April 1896, approval was given for mining, trading and agricultural rights over the 259 sq km (100 sq miles) of territory which lay partly in Bekwai and partly in Adansi. Thus a man with no knowledge of mining acquired what was to turn out to be one of the world's richest gold mines and the largest concession on the Gold Coast.

Cade and his associates registered a new company in the City of London known as the Ashanti Goldfields Corporation Ltd (AGC). On 11 June 1897, the Côte d'Or Mining Company's assets and liabilities were transferred to AGC, and on the same day this new company was listed on the London Stock Exchange with a nominal capital of £250,000 in shares of £1 each.

In early dealings on the London share market, Ashanti £1 shares soared to an incredible £18. For market players who were interested in Africa, the timing was right: investment in South Africa's mines looked increasingly hazardous in the political climate that was to lead to the Boer War.

A year or so later, *The Financial Times* recorded the founders' shareholdings as: E.A. Cade, 6,000; J.E. Biney, 1,110; J.E. Ellis, 770; J.P. Brown, 299. On the death of Edwin Cade in 1903 the shares' value fell sharply, but such was the confidence in the Obuasi goldfield that they soon climbed back to reach £17.

DIFFICULT DAYS AT OBUASI

On 22 November 1897, Cade, along with the mining engineer John Daw and a team of 15 miners, surveyors, fitters and assayers, arrived at Cape Coast Castle. They brought with them 40 tonnes of machinery and equipment, including a five-battery stamp mill, tubular boilers, a sectionalized engine and saw-milling plant, all of which was landed on the beach by canoes that had to battle through dangerous surf. Local carriers, women as well as men, were hired to struggle with the heavy machinery, dismantled into 27-kg (60-lb) headloads, for 200 km (120 miles) through forests, across rivers and along bush paths until they finally arrived at Obuasi on Christmas Eve 1897. For Cade and his team that was when the hard work really began.

"It is doubtful whether any gold-mining venture that has eventually won through to success has been burdened from the start with a greater load of adverse conditions," observed W.R. Feldtmann, John Daw's successor, in *The Mining Magazine* in 1916. Yet, somehow, the forest was cleared for dwellings, the saw mill and the stamp mills were erected and the team got to work.

Apart from the fact that it contained gold, the site's only favourable natural feature was its topography: the hills around Obuasi were ideal for John Daw's policy of adit mining, giving quick, easy and impressive results that led to a boundless optimism about the corporation's future prospects. From March 1898 to June 1899, 3,108 tonnes of ore yielded 2,544 ounces of gold. The next year, 4,673 tonnes yielded 7,812 ounces. In the first

Joseph Ettruson Ellis (1845–1917)

Scratching into the earth had been enough to reveal the gold that gave the Gold Coast its name. But at his Obuasi concession, Joseph Ellis used gunpowder to blast the ore, and Gold Coast mining entered the industrial age.

Ironically, gunpowder was to bring down the curtain on his life: an explosion at his Cape Coast home killed everyone inside and destroyed the meticulous records of his remarkable career. Overwhelmed by the tragedy, he died a few months later, at the age of 72.

Joseph Ettruson Ellis was born in the Central Region village of Kuntu. Like his partner Joseph Biney, he graduated from the Cape Coast Wesleyan School. His family moved to Freetown, Sierra Leone, where he became a tailor. Later, from his tailoring business back in Cape Coast, he observed the hubbub of commerce growing around him, tried his hand as an agent for some of the European firms operating there and eventually became the driving force behind a syndicate of African merchants who bought and sold land and mining concessions. But he and his friend Joseph Biney retained the Obuasi concession: before they established their joint venture with Edwin Cade, their Ellis Mine was the only mine in the Gold Coast owned and operated by Africans.

John Daw began his career in Norway. At AGC, he served as mine superintendent, general manager and consulting engineer before becoming chief executive in 1903.

few years, new discoveries were continually being announced and the erroneous impression arose that many fabulously rich reefs existed beneath the corporation's property. That this was not in fact the case only became clear later, when a systematic survey was made and a reliable picture of the occurrences was obtained.

In the meantime, for Cade and his team, the most important goal was to demonstrate as quickly as possible the promise and value of the property they had purchased. New machinery was readily available. With South Africa now preoccupied with the Anglo-Boer conflict, equipment destined for its mines was diverted to Cape Coast. The partners increased output and convinced the government that the railway line should be extended from Tarkwa up to Obuasi. Work on the railway, however, was not begun in earnest until after the Ashanti uprising against the British of 1900.

TROUBLED TIMES

The effect of the uprising was disastrous: operations were suspended and the workings inevitably suffered from lack of maintenance. There were heavy falls and many of the reef drives collapsed. Some of the ore on the upper levels of the Obuasi reef remains trapped to this day.

13

Wooden, then steel, tramways were soon to make life easier, but at first the quartz was carried from the underground workings by women porters.

Despite the anti-colonial war raging around them, the European staff at Obuasi seem to have escaped the hostilities. White staff remained unharmed at the mines all through the campaign. As a precautionary measure, they built a stockade around the foot of the hill where the Manager's bungalow stood, and still stands, and took up their quarters there for the duration. The rebels allowed one faithful retainer to leave the stockade each day to fetch water for the Europeans. This "sporting spirit" was ascribed to the good relations that Cade and Daw had built up with their local employees.

The arrival of the railway at Obuasi roughly coincided with the start of a

Edwin Cade wrote his first optimistic report on the prospects at "the Obaussie Gold Mine Estate" at Cape Coast Castle. It was there, too, that he signed the agreement to set up the Côte D'Or Mining Company on 27 August 1895.

period of disillusionment. By 1904-5, shareholders dissatisfied with diminishing dividends were becoming sceptical of Daw's promises of higher output. Disappointment was made keener by the high hopes that had earlier prevailed.

In 1905, the Board commissioned W.R. Feldtmann, a leading chemist, and J.A. MacTear, a mining engineer, to carry out an independent assessment of the various mines. Their report was highly critical of the early policy of adit mining off reef drives. They were faced with: "the approaching exhaustion of the most easily accessible ore, previously obtained from adit workings, and a realization that ore bodies above valley level were neither so numerous and extensive nor, in some cases, of such high value as had at first been believed."

Daw shouldered the blame and resigned as Consulting Engineer in favour of Feldtmann. He relinquished his directorship in 1906, ending his contribution of courage and vision on a sad note.

A change of direction

As a result of Feldtmann's report, output was checked for a time in order to allow a vigorous shaft sinking and development programme to be carried out. Henceforth attention was to be directed increasingly to deeper mining. Profits were sacrificed for the next few years and ploughed back into the business. With a rail link to the coastal town of Sekondi, it was now possible to import new improved machinery, including winding engines and headgears. Stores and workshops were built, tramlines in the mines were extended to connect the

Chief Joseph Edward Biney (1849–1937)

In his later years, "Tarkwa Biney" was widely regarded as the wealthiest indigenous Gold Coaster. He was given the honorary appellation "Chief" in recognition of his philanthropy and his encouragement of nationalist causes: often the only way to combat oppressive land and water legislation imposed by the local British administrators was to send delegations to the seat of government in London. Chief Biney might quietly pay their expenses. Born in the village of Anyemaim, near the coastal town of Saltpond, Biney, like his partner Joseph Ellis, attended the Cape Coast Wesleyan School. At the age of 15, he found work as a clerk. His entrepreneurial skills quickly developed, leading to successful business ventures and ultimately to the fateful connection with the London merchants Smith and Cade, for whom he was the West African agent.

different workings, and the surface infrastructure was generally much improved. There was slower progress underground, and the capacity of the new stamp mills was not taxed until the discovery in 1908 of an important deposit that came to be known as Justice's Mine. A few months later, the rich Obuasi shoot was cut at level 3 of the Ashanti mine.

Feldtmann also devoted much thought and experiment to evolving a more satisfactory method of treating the ores. Using his Western Australian experience in dry crushing and roasting preparatory to treatment with cyanide, he had an experimental unit erected and when this proved successful he added two further units so that by 1908 five ball mills and two Edwards roasters were in operation.

Payment of dividends, which had been intermittent in the first 12 years of the mine's existence, became regular only in 1910, although they still fell somewhat short of earlier expectations.

Feldtmann, who was to remain with the company for 20 years, introduced a new, more scientific approach and, in a way, a new era. From then on, reflecting a general trend in the evolution of business in the 20th century, the story of the Ashanti mine would focus less on personalities and a pioneering spirit than on a hard-headed struggle for growth in a mechanized and troubled world.

SURVIVING TWO WORLD WARS

A shortage of European staff and stores during the First World War (1914–18) meant cutting back production, concentrating on the profitable Ashanti mine and closing Ayenim and Justice's mines. Because of soaring working costs at the end of that war, it was not until 1933 that these two mines could be reopened.

After the war, an extraordinary cocoa boom became the Gold Coast's major commercial preoccupation. At the Ashanti goldfields, a shortage of labour for cutting firewood led to the abandonment of dry crushing. However, experiments with wet crushing were so unsuccessful that the old process was restored in 1924. Until the outbreak of the Second World War in 1939, each year showed an increase in tonnage treated and in gold output.

In the early years of the Second World War it was possible to continue work and an impressive 12,702 m (41,6730 ft) out of 18,288 m (60,000 ft) of development was achieved in the Ashanti mine alone. Important discoveries made in 1937 on the Obuasi fissure meant that from 1938 on developments concentrated on proving the reef in depth rather than laterally.

Results of other explorations gave grounds for considerable optimism and justified budgeting for an increase in output. Plans were made to sink new shafts, build an aerial ropeway to connect all shafts with the treatment plant and begin a programme of large-scale reforestation. Work on these projects began as early as 1938 but was interrupted at the end of 1941 when a shortage of specialist staff and supplies once again brought progress to a standstill.

The Second World War inevitably had a profound influence not only on the Ashanti goldfields but also on the entire gold mining industry in the then Gold Coast. In fact most mines were closed down, except for a few profitable ones, including AGC, which were placed on a "care and maintenance" system. The dozen or so mines that remained operational survived on rather obsolete equipment since management could not obtain additional capital for refurbishment.

Nonetheless, G.W. Eaton Turner, the author of a short history celebrating the corporation's Jubilee in 1947, was able to end on an upbeat note, recording that from the beginning of operations until September 1946, the mines operated by AGC had produced 5,872,855 tonnes yielding 5,751,008 ounces of gold. Of this the Gold Coast government received one ounce out of every 20 recovered, a royalty which had so far amounted to more than £1.75 million. Twice that had been paid by AGC in export duty on gold premium. This, along with the payment of wages to local workers, as well as payments for customs duties and other services, meant that the corporation made a substantial direct and indirect contribution to the economic prosperity of the Gold Coast.

John White PHO *Edwin A. Cade — May 18 1895.* IPSWICH.

Edwin Arthur Cade (1856–1903)

With his flaming red hair and full beard, Edwin Cade was a figure of wonderment to his African partners and workers. Behind those features was concealed an ambition expressed in foresight, courage and determination. It was Cade who in London recognized the potential significance of the assayer's report on a sample of Obuasi ore and immediately took ship to Cape Coast; it was Cade who gave this local enterprise its international presence.

Born in Ipswich, England, he was first apprenticed to the family photography business. His marriage to the daughter of a London merchant with West African interests, C. Smith, brought him the partnership, in 1892, which renamed the company Smith and Cade.

But the Gold Coast venture which made his career ended his life. He died of malaria at the age of 46 in the Offin River village of Dominassi. He is buried in the European cemetery at Obuasi.

Headloads of gold bars begin their journey to London by rail to the port of Sekondi. Today, the company aircraft takes the bullion to Accra, where it changes planes to go to the final processing plant in Switzerland.

ASHANTI IN THE DOLDRUMS

Despite the country's gold potential, it seemed impossible to shake off the post-war stagnation that had beset the gold mining industry. Since 1942 it had been unable to attract any major foreign investment or participation. Many mines that had opened during the second "jungle boom" (an African post-war equivalent of the American gold rushes) had closed down and many exploration ventures were postponed. Only four mines remained in operation, of which the most important was AGC.

Throughout this period, the company's nominal and distant leader was General Sir Edward Spears, Chairman from 1937 until 1973. Spears treated the business as a personal fiefdom. He spent little time in the country. When he did visit, his style was to indulge leaders such as the then Prime Minister, Dr Kwame Nkrumah, blurring the fact that the company was by now paying derisory royalties to the government – about £9,000 a year.

In 1966, the first military government, the National Liberation Council, began to query the contribution of AGC and other mining concessions to the local economy. When General Spears realized that AGC's leases might not be renewed on the same terms as before, his response was to

A panoramic view of the AGC concession, photographed about 60 years ago. As prospecting techniques became more sophisticated, workable ore was identified under the camp sites shown here and some of the buildings have now been demolished to make way for mining.

threaten to flood the mines. The Commissioner of Mines and Energy, R. Sylvan Amegashie, was mandated by General Ankrah's government to seek potential new investors in Ghana's mining industry.

THE LONRHO TAKE-OVER

Coincidentally, an outside party was already assessing the potential of AGC. Action quickly followed. R.W. "Tiny" Rowland's company Lonrho (London and Rhodesia Mining and Land Company), a multinational conglomerate with a particular interest in prospecting and mining in Africa, began its acquisition of the company, leading to its delisting on the London Stock Exchange.

The cost to Lonrho was £3 million, plus a limited share issue, for a mine that many experts considered to be in the last two or three years of useful life. In return for granting a 50-year extension of the land leases, the Ghana government received 20 percent of the company with an option to acquire another 20 percent at the fixed price of £1 a share.

After the coup led by Colonel Ignatius Acheampong which, in January 1972,

toppled Dr K.A. Busia's democratically elected government, the state acquired by decree 55 percent of all mining companies. The Ashanti Goldfields Corporation, which was to become the Ashanti Goldfields Company, was ordered to transfer its head office from London to Accra.

During this turbulent period, the company's autocratic chairman, Sir Edward Spears, was deposed by Lonrho. The government appointed as its representative on the Board of AGC Lloyd A.K. Quashie, a distinguished Ghanaian geologist with an expert understanding of mining. As Deputy Managing Director, Quashie paid particular attention to improving the conditions and prospects of indigenous staff. Promising young Ghanaians were sent overseas to further their education, to qualify them to take over the so-called expatriate positions. Among the first beneficiaries of the programme was Sam E. Jonah, the current Chief Executive of AGC.

CHANGING FORTUNES

In 1972, gold production at Ashanti peaked at 533,00 ounces, but output rapidly declined in the rest of that decade. A

Photographed at the time of the acquisition of AGC, Lonrho's proprietor, Tiny Rowland, is flanked by General Ankrah (in uniform), then Chairman of Ghana's National Liberation Council, and Sylvan Amegashie, then Commissioner of Mines and Energy.

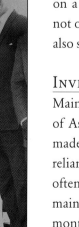

number of the higher grade shoots were exhausted, and high taxes, a lack of foreign exchange, a tightly controlled economy and an overvalued currency all made it impossible for AGC to buy spare or replacement parts or to invest in new plant. By the end of this economically and politically troubled decade, annual production had fallen to 232,000 ounces.

When Flight Lieutenant Jerry John Rawlings' military regime assumed power in 1982, the situation began to improve. As part of an Economic Recovery Programme overseen by the Minister of Finance, Dr Kwesi Botchwey, the government took steps to create a more favourable climate for investment in Ghana. The programme was launched in 1983 with the backing of the International Monetary Fund, the World Bank and Western aid donors: its prime goal was the rehabilitation of the country's major export earners, one of which, of course, was gold.

As a result, in 1985 AGC was granted a much-needed shot in the arm – a loan of $159 million to fund an ambitious five-year schedule of expansion and improvement. The project was financed by a consortium of banks led by the International Finance Corporation, the World Bank's private sector affiliate, which specializes in the support of viable commercial enterprises in developing countries. In addition, the government of Ghana passed a new Minerals and Mining Law, which would allow AGC to retain 45 percent of its export earnings; this additional source of capital was essential for the success of the project, enabling the company to repay its loans and invest for future expansion.

Sam Jonah, the company's new Managing Director, the first Ghanaian Chief Executive, appointed in 1986, oversaw the turn of the tide. He endorsed the investment project's target of a return to 400,000 ounces of gold a year within three years.

As well as the programme of shaft sinking and development, AGC embarked on a three-year programme to modernize not only the mine and treatment plant but also services and the general infrastructure.

INVESTING IN INFRASTRUCTURE

Maintaining and operating a mine the size of Ashanti is a formidable task, which is made even more difficult because it is so reliant on imports. Because shipping is often irregular, the mine is obliged to maintain stock levels sufficient for six months' gold production of literally thousands of items, including chemicals

shortages in the early 1980s, developed livestock and fish-farming activities.

With a workforce numbering 10,000, the company's commitments clearly extend to the social infrastructure within the local townships. As well as providing housing, educational, recreational and health facilities for its workers, AGC undertakes the building of new roads and the maintenance of old ones. The company's energetic programme of activities in these areas is described more fully in Chapter 2.

EXPANSION AND DEVELOPMENT

The shaft-sinking and development programme begun in 1985–86 was intended to provide access to the three main sources of ore that AGC planned to mine over the following 12 years. This included the George Cappendell shaft, named for Lonrho's consulting engineer. By 1987, the year of Cappendell's death, the shaft (for both men and materials) at the southern end of the mine had been sunk and concrete-lined to a depth of 853 m (2,800 ft). It was commissioned that same year by Flight Lieutenant Rawlings, then Chairman of the Provisional National Defence Council government. Two more ventilation shafts were also to be provided at the southern end of the mine.

An extensive new conveyor system was constructed in order to transport ore from the southern end of the mine, and the underground compressed air circulation system was to be upgraded. New and larger capacity mine cars were introduced, as were additional underground locomotives.

Flight Lieutenant Rawlings, wearing combat uniform, opens the George Cappendell Shaft in 1987. On his left is Annan Cato, then Chief of State Protocol and now Ghana's High Commissioner to Canada; on his right is Colonel Osei Owusu, then Minister of the Interior.

and explosives. Before the Akosombo Dam was commissioned in 1965, the mine also had to generate its own power.

Massive investment is needed not only to pursue essential ongoing repair programmes but also to purchase new, improved plant and equipment. AGC's own timber concessions, which of course need to be maintained, worked and re-planted, supply all the timber required for the mine as well as firewood needed for the roasters at the treatment plant. In order to be as self-reliant as possible, the mine also maintains extensive workshop and transport facilities. It runs a farm growing fruit and vegetables and, during food

General Sir Edward Spears (1886–1974)

Edward Spears distinguished himself in two world wars. Wounded in action four times during the First World War, he earned the highest military honours including the French Croix de Guerre. In the Second World War, he played a key role in the rise of Charles de Gaulle, leader of the Free French forces and later President of France. Appointed Chairman of AGC in 1937, Spears' aristocratic style later became increasingly autocratic and eccentric. He spent just two months a year in Ghana, and contemporary photographs show him in pith helmet, white double-breasted suit, carrying a cane like an officer's baton and with uniformed guards following the required one pace behind.

The style was not to the taste of the company's new owners, Lonrho, and Spears was replaced in 1973.

Improvements and innovations at the Pompora treatment plant (in operation since 1947), including the installation of new crushers, were designed to lead to a significant increase in recovery. Also part of the Pompora rehabilitation plan was the $6 million tailings treatment plant, built to recoup gold from the 13.8 million tonnes of tailings generated over the course of 90 years' production.

AGC IN THE NINETIES

The 1985 programme of expansion and modernization was to continue into the nineties. In 1990 new mining equipment was purchased for mining surface oxides at Sansu and a new heap leach plant was commissioned. During March 1991 a new oxide treatment plant (to treat ore from the Sansu open-pit operations) came on line. With the help of International Finance Corporation loans, production soared to record levels in 1992, but it had already become clear that if increased levels were to be sustained still further investment would be needed.

For this reason the Ashanti Mines Expansion Programme (AMEP) was initiated, again financed by the IFC, with an annual target of 1.0 Moz (one million ounces) by 1995. The main thrust of the programme was to enable Ashanti

General Spears strides to the opening of Obuasi's new mosque in 1951. Whenever the local labour supply could not meet the mine's requirements, Muslims were recruited from neighbouring northern countries. The community has taken root in Obuasi.

Ashanti's pan-African Ambitions

By the year 2000, one-third – 500,000 ounces – of the Ashanti Goldfields Company's annual production will come from African countries outside Ghana. Although the decision to exploit the sub-Saharan mineralization belt wherever it led was taken only three years ago, an impressive portfolio of assets throughout Africa has already been acquired. Corporate acquisitions, strategic alliances and aggressive exploration programmes have given the company a stake in more than 35 projects in 14 countries.

Mali
Ashanti has investigated the Kalana Mine project and is also reviewing other licences.

Senegal
AGC is actively prospecting at properties in Bambadji and other areas.

Guinea
The Siguiri project will commence production in 1998. Costing more than $50 million, this mine is billed to become the largest gold mine in the country.

Côte d'Ivoire
AGC has been invited to prospect for gold in this potentially rich country.

Burkina Faso
AGC is actively prospecting the Youga concession with Echo Bay Mines.

Angola
The Company has obtained its first licence here with the restoration of peace in this mineral-rich country.

Niger
AGC has the largest exploration landholding in this country.

Eritrea
The Company has been investigating two concessions in this country.

Ethiopia
Exploration activities in the Tigray province are being undertaken in a joint venture with EZANA Mining Development, Limited.

Tanzania
Re-evaluation of the old Geita Mine has led to the delineation of 3 million oz. Feasibility studies have commenced. Ashanti has several other projects in partnership with other mining companies.

Democratic Republic of Congo
AGC is discussing a number of gold projects with the government.

Mozambique
Ashanti is prospecting on four licences in this country.

Zimbabwe
The Freda Rebecca Mine, the largest in the country, produces about 100,000 oz a year, following the measures taken after the Cluff acquisition.

The latest gold mine constructed in Ghana by the Ashanti Group is at **Bibiani.**

Ayanfuri, originally owned by the British mining company Cluff Resources, is run as a satellite of the famous AGC mine at Obuasi.

Iduapriem, originally owned by the Australian company GSM, has been greatly upgraded by Ashanti.

Obuasi will continue to account for the majority of AGC output well into the 21st century.

R.W. "Tiny" Rowland (1917–)

Born in India, educated in Germany and England, Tiny Rowland launched his adventurous business career from a family background of international trading. His first job, in his grandfather's shipping and forwarding firm in the City of London, sent him on prewar travels throughout Eastern Europe.

His remarkable African odyssey began with his first visit to the continent in 1947. Experience of farming and the mining of metallurgical chrome, copper, gold, emeralds and platinum were the background to his establishment of Lonrho (London and Rhodesia Mining and Land Company) in 1961. Lonrho was the vehicle for Rowland's purchase of the Ashanti Goldfields Corporation in 1969.

Rowland has created more than 800 companies, mostly in Africa. His support for independent national empowerment of former colonial territories began when his friend Krishna Menon involved him in Gandhi's India League. In 1996, South Africa's president, Nelson Mandela, decorated him, right, for his long-term assistance to liberation movements in Africa and for his role in the Mozambique peace process.

to exploit the large, lower grade underground resources which had been identified as the ones most likely to be profitable in the long term. AMEP required $550 million investment and this was raised partly by a syndicated loan arranged by the IFC, partly from AGC's own funds and partly from the IFC itself.

The programme included the further upgrading of the Pompora treatment plant, the accessing of sulphide ore from the surface at Sansu, and underground modernization. The most crucial element of the programme was the construction of a new sulphide treatment plant using the latest technology which harnessed bacteria

to oxidize the ore. The Biox® plant came into production in early 1994 and uses *Thiobacillus ferro-oxidans* to separate gold from ore.

Dubbed "rock-eating gold bugs", the bacteria cause chemical changes that break the sulphide bonds in the ore and release the gold. After these "bugs" have completed their work, which takes about four days, around 90 percent of the gold is released. The toxic arsenic and sulphur compounds that are usually released in other forms of processing are rendered in stable forms. Ashanti chose this bio-leaching process over other processes because it is one of the most environmentally friendly ways of extracting gold from ore. The Biox® plant is now responsible for all the gold produced at the Obuasi mine.

AN INTERNATIONAL COMPANY

In 1994 the Ghana government, the majority shareholder, announced plans to sell 20–25 percent of its interest in AGC in a share flotation, and the company was listed on the London and Ghana stock exchanges. It was the largest flotation

The head office of the Ashanti Goldfields Company in Accra.

On the trading floor of the New York Stock Exchange, left to right, Nana Oduro Numapau, President of the Ghana National House of Chiefs; Sam Jonah, AGC Chief Executive; Richard Grasso, NYSE Chief Executive; and Mark Keatley, AGC's Chief Financial Officer, express their delight at the listing of Ashanti on the big board.

organized by any gold mining company – the co-ordinating and advisory team alone numbered over 200 people. Each of the company's 10,000 employees received five free shares.

By 1995, Richard K. Peprah, Chairman of AGC, the present Minister of Finance who was then Minister of Mines and Energy, was able to report that after its first complete year as an international public company, AGC had "witnessed further solid growth in [its] reserves and resources". And Chief Executive Sam Jonah could observe with satisfaction that "gold production at Obuasi [had] risen at a compound rate of 15 percent since 1985 when Ashanti embarked on its strategy of modernization and growth".

The New York Stock Exchange showed its faith in Jonah's well-placed confidence when AGC was listed there to raise new capital in 1996. It was the first African company to appear on Wall Street.

Production from the Obuasi mine continued to increase, thanks to the introduction of mechanized mining methods using larger equipment. By the end of 1994 the fourth train of Biox® reactors had been commissioned, making this the largest plant in the world using state of the art Biox® technology. The Pompora treatment plant continued to perform well, with increased output, and further expansion and refinements of the plant were proposed.

To identify future surface and underground resources, AGC embarked on a coordinated geological, geophysical and geochemical assessment with a team of international specialists. Hi-tech aids to

Samuel Esson Jonah *(1949–)*

In the year that Lonrho acquired AGC, 1969, Sam Jonah joined the company as a labourer straight from high school. The following year he won company sponsorship to travel to Britain to study at the Camborne School of Mines and then at London University's Imperial College.

Back at Obuasi, his leadership qualities were quickly recognized: he became a shift boss, then mine captain, underground manager, senior engineer, general manager and deputy managing director. At the age of 36 he became the first African Chief Executive of AGC and a full member of the board of Lonrho.

Jonah grew up in the shadow of the headgear at Obuasi, where his father ran a building business. He represents the interests of his industry and his country on a wide range of commissions, funds and corporate boards. Jonah returned to Camborne in 1996 to receive the award of an honorary doctorate, the first alumnus – and only the second person – ever to have received such an award. In 1992, the Ghana Trade Union Congress named him "National Worker of the Year".

detection included the use of aerial photography as a basis for geological interpretation and a helicopter-borne electromagnetic geophysical survey. The findings were encouraging and led to serious investment in expanding underground production, while production from large-scale surface operations was scaled down.

A GOLDEN FUTURE

The mine at Obuasi has been in continual production for 100 years, and the ore body continues to be highly prospective, with proven and probable reserves estimated to be more than 20 million ounces. AGC's plans and investments have the aim of maintaining group production at around one million ounces per year, and Sam Jonah is confident he will meet this target.

Ashanti operates one of the largest and richest gold mines in the world. At its present production rate, it will remain one of the top ten gold producers for a long time to come.

But AGC now has new horizons: no longer a gold producer with a single mine in Ghana, it has operating, exploration and development projects on many of the most promising gold mineralization belts of sub-Saharan Africa. The future certainly looks golden.

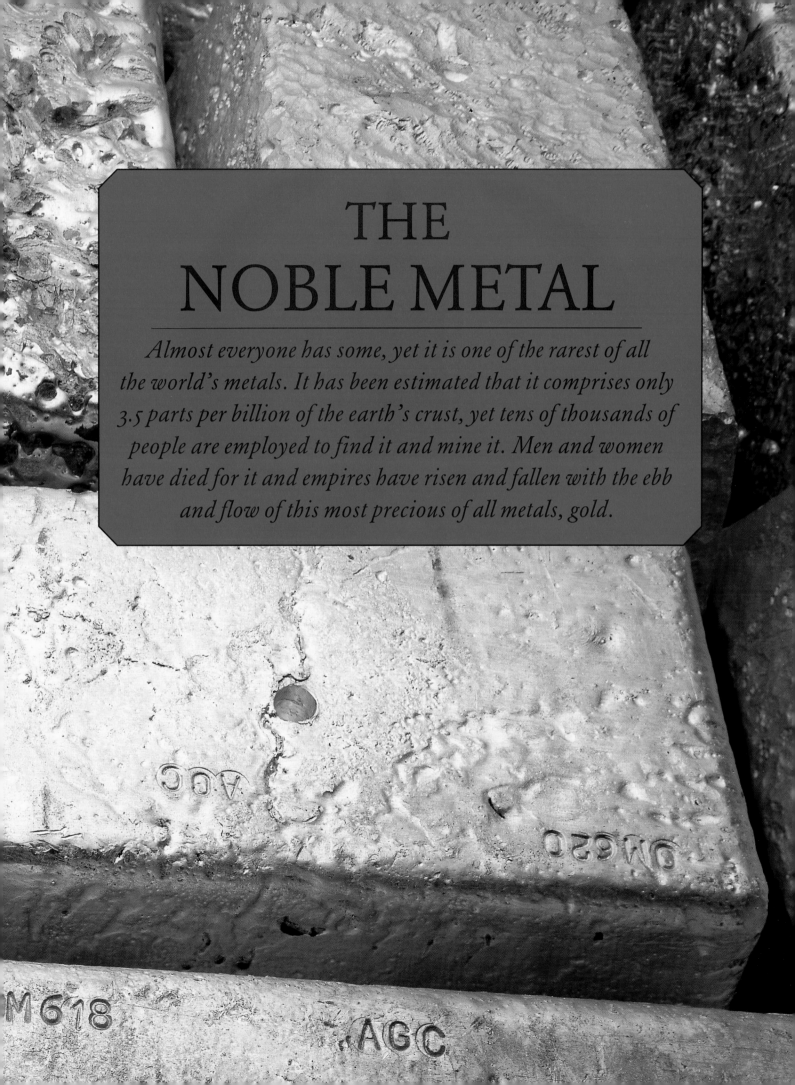

THE NOBLE METAL

Almost everyone has some, yet it is one of the rarest of all the world's metals. It has been estimated that it comprises only 3.5 parts per billion of the earth's crust, yet tens of thousands of people are employed to find it and mine it. Men and women have died for it and empires have risen and fallen with the ebb and flow of this most precious of all metals, gold.

THE NOBLE METAL

"For thousands of years people have desired it and sought it out, esteeming it the most precious of all metals. It is a prized possession in all countries, in all cultures and in all the ages of history."

Gold is extraordinary. Throughout the bumpy course of history, people have used it to glorify their temples, to adorn their rulers with splendour, to create things of high value and to make great works of art. Over the centuries, it has been fashioned into coins and jewellery, and into an infinity of other objects, many of which have been transported around the world, buried, lost and recovered – the metal melted down and re-used. Gold has been traded, stolen, plundered and smuggled all over the globe.

There seem to be inherent qualities in this metal which entrance us, which make us want to possess it. People of all races and ranks have given their lives for it and for the wealth and power that it promises to bring. They have travelled around the world to search for it, toiling to win a few precious grains of the metal from river sands, or precariously burrowing beneath the earth to extract it. Even today, gold miners penetrate thousands of metres underground to reach gold-bearing strata, extracting thousands of tonnes of material from which only a few ounces of gold will eventually be recovered, using the most elaborate and complex processes.

Until recently, gold was used to glorify the objects and people it adorned. It was also used to make coins, which not only had intrinsic value but could be used to put a value on a vast range of other things,

The Ashanti ceremonial helmet is made of antelope skin and is decorated with golden jaw bones and trophy heads. The top is decorated with golden horns.

making them exchangeable. Today, gold has a myriad uses; for example, it protects fragile humans when they venture into the freezing wastes of space and it ensures the efficiency of innumerable electronic items on which many of us now depend. It is used in medicine for the treatment of cancer, and in architecture it keeps glass-clad buildings cool. It is used in jet engines and on the windscreens of aircraft to maintain visibility at altitude. Works of art are created with it and it is still used as an embellishment in a wide range of situations. Gold coins and bullion bars are still used to facilitate the international exchange of goods and services. Above all, it remains the ultimate expression of value and wealth all over the world.

THE SWEAT OF THE SUN

Gold today, as much as in the past, is a metal which seems to embody the warmth and brightness, the power and the strength, of the sun. The Inca of South America, once skilled finders and miners of gold and consummate metal-smiths, referred to gold as "The Sweat of the Sun", contrasting its warmth with the coolness of the more common metal silver – "The Tears of the Moon". The Ashantis, great users and workers of gold, used gold dust as their everyday currency until a hundred years ago. Dead chiefs and wealthy citizens were often covered with gold dust and buried. This custom has interesting parallels with the ancient Egyptian burial customs. The Ashantis call the metal *sika kokoo*, meaning "red gold", an adjective signifying a warm, powerful material. The

chemical symbol for gold, Au, derived from the Latin word *aurum*, is linked to early Indo-European words that mean "Dawn of Day", once again emphasizing the qualities of warmth and light. Gold and the sun, the warmth of gold and life itself, seem inextricably linked in the thinking of many cultures.

The word "golden" is often applied to the things we value most or most desire. One powerful Western myth is that of the Golden Age, a time of peace and plenty, which existed before the ever-accelerating decay of human society began. The golden rule, the golden section and the golden age – gold has become a metaphor for all that is best.

THE PUREST METAL

We do not know exactly when people first began to seek out gold and make use of it, but it is probable that, in some parts of the world at least, it was the first metal they knew. This must have been due to

two basic characteristics of gold. First, it can be found as a native, or pure, metal, that is, as nuggets or as gold dust rather than combined with other elements from which it must be extracted. Second, gold is completely resistant to corrosion and oxidation, which cause other metals, such as tin and iron, to weaken, corrode and eventually disintegrate. This means that however long it may lie in a river or rest on the surface of the soil, its natural brightness and colour are unaltered and undiminished, its rich glow remains unclouded.

Gold crystals, below left, are typically found within veins of quartz. Large, well-formed crystals would indicate that the gold formed within a large rock cavity.

When the tomb of Tutankhamen, *the Egyptian pharaoh was opened in 1922, the incredible amount of gold it contained was still untarnished after thousands of years.*

In many parts of the world the glittering metal is there for the finding; unlike many other metals, gold does not need to be smelted. Deep in the earth, native gold is enclosed within deposits of extremely hard quartz. It may appear in a variety of forms within the rock, sometimes shaped like delicate leaves or strange plants, at other times as sharp-edged crystals or tiny flakes. However, after millions of years of weathering by water and wind, and by the alternation of cold and heat, the gold is gradually set free. As the surrounding rock almost imperceptibly disintegrates, the metal is separated from it. In this way, lumps of the pure gold are eventually carried towards the surface soil or are washed down in the sand and gravel of streams and rivers. Some of these lumps of gold may be as large as a fist, but most are little bigger than tiny grains or flakes. Thus the metal is released and distributed away from the geological strata in which it was first formed and is made accessible to those who can recognize its presence.

Gold, the noblest of metals, is highly resistant to chemical attack, that is to say, it is not easily altered so its appearance always remains the same. It does not combine with oxygen, except in the most unusual of circumstances, or with sulphur. It is unaffected by chlorine, bromine and fluorine, which would corrode other metals, and remains chemically unchanged by any single acid. The bright glint of a nugget protruding from a bank of gravel at a stream's edge, or the shimmer of gold dust amidst a layer of sand, would have attracted the attention of early humans. It is due to this characteristic that objects made from gold, such as those recovered from the tomb of the Egyptian pharaoh Tutankhamen, were as bright and glowing on the day they were found as when they were buried over three thousand years before. Today, this same incorruptibility of gold remains one of its most precious and useful physical attributes, favouring its use in many circumstances where lesser metals would corrode and decay.

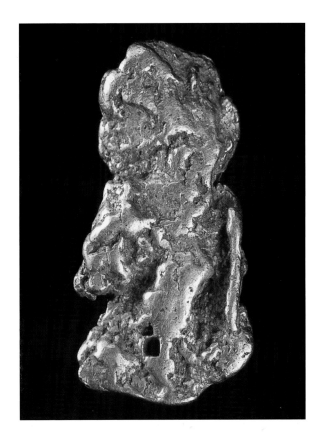

Although gold may start off in a crystalline form, the nugget above shows how it looks after weathering and erosion have taken their toll. This nugget contains copper, which gives it a red colour.

GOLD COMPOUNDS

In certain circumstances, however, gold does form a number of compounds, although some of these can only be achieved under laboratory conditions. Some of the most important naturally occurring gold compounds are often formed with the element tellurium and are called gold tellurides. These compounds are mainly found around Kalgoorlie in Western Australia and in Colorado and California in North America. They are now mined for the gold that they contain. One compound, krennerite, contains between 30 and 43 percent gold; another, calaverite, about 40 percent; while sylvanite has up to 28 percent. Gold is also often found mixed in very

Gold is a soft, malleable metal. *In this nugget the well-worn gold has moulded itself around the contours of the rock on which it formed.*

small quantities associated with deposits of lead and copper and is recovered during the refining process used to extract those metals. There are, however, sources of gold which are totally uneconomical to exploit. Gold is found in the wood and bark of some trees growing in gold-bearing regions, for example; in Colorado some trees contain as much as three parts per million of gold. Gold is also present in sea water in such a huge quantity that if all the gold in all the seas and oceans were added together it would total many hundreds of tonnes. However, disappointingly, in any million million units of water there are less than six units of gold. Extracting gold from the sea, therefore, would cost far more than it would be worth.

GOLD'S CHEMICAL PROPERTIES

We now understand far more about the physical and chemical properties of gold and how they create its qualities. The metal itself is an element, one of a group of 56 metals occupying the central block of the periodic table. This means that it is not a mixture or compound of other substances. Like most metals the atomic structure is known as a close-packed cube, where the atoms are arranged as a cube, with a further atom at the centre of each face. Crystals of gold have a hexagonal or cubic form. It has the high atomic weight of 196.967 and a specific gravity of 19.3; in practical terms this means that a lump of gold is extremely heavy for its size. A better sense of its mass can be gained by considering the fact that a standard gold ingot, which measures 175 x 90 x 40 mm (7 x 3½ x 1½ in), weighs 12.45 kg (27 lb) – so people attempting to smuggle a few gold bars under their clothing would have to be very strong!

Gold has a melting point of 1,063°C (1,945°F), which is a little lower than that of copper, 1,083°C (1,981°F), and higher than that of silver, 961°C (1,762°F). For long periods of human history, it has been possible for metal workers to attain the melting point of gold in fairly simple furnaces, using charcoal for fuel and hand-bellows to pump air through them. Roughly the same temperature level was needed to smelt iron and copper and the technology to achieve it was known and understood in many parts of the world. Most importantly, heat of this intensity could be used to turn solid gold into its liquid form so that it could be poured and cast into new shapes. Because this level of heat was relatively easy to achieve, masterpieces of cast-gold work could be created by goldsmiths working with the simplest of tools and equipment.

Another equally important characteristic of gold that sets it apart from other metals is the fact that, unlike most other metals, it does not oxidize when it is heated. Those working with gold soon learned that however many times they melted and re-melted it, they ended up with virtually the same quantity of the metal. When copper, silver, tin or lead were melted down, the hot metal became oxidized and the amount of metal remaining after the process was decreased.

There is a striking paradox about the physical nature and the inherent qualities of gold. In its pure form the metal is extremely soft – so soft that it can be scratched or cut very easily, and bent

The Latrobe nugget *is a 717-g (25-oz) mass of crystallized cubes 11 cm (4⅓ in) high.*

or twisted by using simple tools and little effort. It has little tensile strength and cannot be used to make anything that has to take a strain. Yet, while gold is easy to manipulate and shape, it is, as we have seen, also extremely chemically unreactive. It retains its colour and shine, it does not become oxidized or form other compounds which would alter its appearance. To the people who first began to use this metal, this must have added to its attraction.

PHYSICAL PROPERTIES

The structure of gold allows it to be stretched into wire or hammered into sheets so that it can become vastly extended without breaking down or changing its character. The high malleability of gold has been utilized in numerous ways over the centuries. It must have been one of the first characteristics of the metal that humans exploited for their own

Gold can be beaten so thin that it becomes almost transparent. This is an example of hammered gold sheet. Hammered gold can also be decorated and shaped by beating it with special tools.

purposes. Pieces of gold can be fused together by hammering and the new mass that results can then be shaped into further new forms by more hammering and blending. Beating separate pieces of gold together to produce sheets has another important effect, or rather a non-effect: the nature of the gold is not altered.

Other metals, when they are repeatedly hammered, change in important ways. Copper can be hardened by hammering, for example, making it much more useful for weapons or cutting-tools, and iron becomes magnetized by the process. Gold, however, remains unchanged. Working with it in this way is comparatively easy, although the metal

needs to be heated and cooled from time to time to stop it becoming brittle.

From foil to filament

So great is its malleability that gold can be beaten out into sheets one fourteen thousandth of a millimetre thick, so thin that they can be seen through and so delicate that they float away on a breath of air. A little gold can be made to go a very long way: 31.1 g (1 troy ounce) of gold, for example, can be beaten out into a film that will cover 28 sq m (300 sq ft). Gold, when it is beaten thinly enough, becomes virtually transparent, imparting a greenish tint to light that is transmitted through it. Yet no matter how fine a gold sheet may be, it still conducts electricity extremely efficiently. This fact was utilized by the French car designer Ettore Bugatti in the 1930s. He sandwiched a transparent film of gold between two sheets of glass for the windscreen of his most luxurious model; when a current was

passed through the metal, it heated and demisted the screen.

Usually, gold sheet and gold foil are used to adorn things made of cheaper material, to bring richness to the otherwise mundane. Gold leaf has been used to decorate the spines of books, the frames of paintings, and even the plaster ceilings and decorative ironwork of palaces. There, it neither tarnishes nor decays, often retaining its richness long after what it adorned has begun to rot away.

Gold can also be drawn out into wire, which is to say it is highly ductile. The goldsmiths of many ancient civilizations used to pull the metal through increasingly small holes drilled through an iron or bronze plate, or dragged it through notches cut into any unyielding substance. The ancient Egyptians were among those who made gold wire and wove it into cloth. The manufacture of gold cloth later became one of the ways the richest societies of the Orient and Europe flaunted the wealth of their

Gold's ductile quality means it can be drawn out into the thinnest of threads. This sumptuous fabric, part of a late 18th-century Chinese surcoat, is embroidered with fine gold thread.

The throne of Tutankhamen is covered in gold sheet. The gold is decorated with embossed patterns and hieroglyphs – in a technique known as repoussé.

This illuminated manuscript dates from the 14th century. It is decorated with gold leaf fixed to parchment. One of the earliest examples of illuminated manuscripts, the Lindisfarne Gospels, was produced in 721 AD.

The electrum coin, right, one of the first made with an inscription, comes from Lydia and dates from between 600 and 575 BC. The first gold coins were also made there in c. 560 BC.

leaders. Today, gold can be mechanically stretched to produce filaments finer than the finest human hair and a single troy ounce can be made into 80 km (50 miles) of fine gold wire.

MAKING MONEY

Most gold, when it is found, is in naturally alloyed forms, most commonly with silver, copper, platinum and palladium. Silver and gold, for example, can exist together, with one atom of silver replacing one atom of gold in any proportion. Gold is often found with 10 to 15 percentage of silver by weight. The presence of silver alters the colour of the metal, making it a paler and paler yellow as the amount of silver increases.

When gold contains about 20 to 35 percent silver it is known as electrum. This naturally occurring metal was used in one of the most important human inventions. In western Asia Minor, around 640 BC, small lumps of electrum were marked with punches to stamp them with a common character and the first coins were thus created. The minting of coins not only became a sign of a centralized state and an indication of a ruler's wealth and power, but it reflected the way in which the control of important sources of gold shifted as one group conquered or displaced another, or discovered new mines.

Alexander the Great's father, Philip II of Macedon, issued large numbers of gold coins named after himself when new mines were opened in his territory. His son minted even more when his destruction of the Persian Empire in 330 BC brought large quantities of gold into his hands. Similarly Spain's access to the gold and silver mines of the New World following the arrival of Columbus in 1492 led to a vast expansion of Spanish coinage and to the quantities of these metals in circulation in Europe.

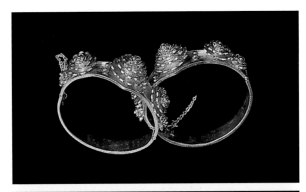

Modern Ashanti jewellery *continues a long tradition of superb craftsmanship. The bracelets and necklace show typically exquisite working of the noble metal.*

This 18-karat gold handbag *is made from gold mesh, which is fine gold wire formed into links. It is decorated with semi-precious stones.*

Others shared in Spain's discoveries in a more direct way – by lying in wait to attack and plunder her annual treasure fleets as they plied the ocean or by mounting surprise raids on the towns where the gold was being stored ready for transportation to Spain. Some of the gold that adorned King Henry VIII and his daughter Elizabeth I came to England by that route.

In the 15th, 16th and 17th centuries, gold from the mines of West Africa, in the region Europeans appropriately called the Gold Coast because of the vast amounts of gold there, was also brought back to Europe by Portuguese, Dutch, British and other traders. This, too, was minted into coins and, by passing into circulation, assisted the growth of the European economies.

ERODING VALUES

The relative softness of gold made the creation of early coins an easy process. These were made by striking a standard weight of gold with a die made of a harder metal, usually bronze or iron. Both the die and the anvil that the gold rested on were engraved with a design. When the die was struck with a hammer both faces of the malleable gold were squeezed into the engraved areas. In this way the engraved "negative" designs cut into die and anvil were converted into raised areas on the coin forming its front and back.

The one disadvantage in the making of these coins (given the softness of gold, even when alloyed with other metals) was that the metal wore away. Over time, the weight of the coin, and hence its

value, would imperceptibly diminish. Its thin edges would get thinner, the designs on its faces would become less and less distinct. In addition, dishonest people took advantage of this natural process by filing or clipping metal from the circumference of the coin, a crime that was punishable by death in some European countries in the Middle Ages.

WEIGHTS AND MEASURES

If gold is to be alloyed with less valuable metals there clearly needs to be some standardized way to indicate the amount of gold that is present. For this purpose, the karat system is now widely used. The term itself is derived from the carob beans originally used as weights for gold in the Classical and Islamic worlds. Traditionally there were differing values attributed to these weights in the different regions, but in 1914 the value of the metric karat was fixed at 0.2 g (0.007 oz). Pure gold is classed as 24 karat, a metal containing 75 percent gold is 18-karat gold, and when the metal contains only half gold it is 12 karat. The system is useful in so far as it indicates how much of the most valuable metal is present but, of

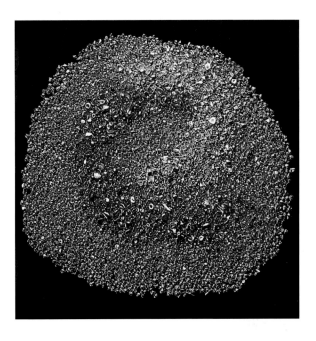

Anything less than 24-karat gold is an alloy. The various quantities of gold, silver and copper, above, show the proportions of each in 18-karat gold.

The touchstone, below, is used to test the purity of gold. For the untrained eye, the different colours produced by varying purities of gold are sometimes difficult to distinguish.

course, it does not give any information about what other metal or metals are mixed in with it. This lack of clarity is further compounded by the fact that karats, as units of weight, are also used in the diamond industry.

Alloying gold with other metals not only hardens it but also changes its colour, which is, therefore, a good indicator of its purity. This fact has long been used as the basis for the touchstone test. A touchstone is a hard, very smooth-grained stone, usually medium to dark brown or black in colour. If a piece of gold is rubbed against the touchstone it will leave a yellow streak on it, the width of which will depend on the hardness of the metal and the pressure exerted. The purity of the gold can then be judged by the colour of the line left on the surface of the touchstone. This

is done either by comparing it with similar nearby lines made on the stone with gold of known degrees of purity, or simply by experience. Even though the method seems crude, a skilled user can get very accurate results.

The troy grain, troy pennyweight, troy ounce and troy pound are elements of the traditional European system, used since the Middle Ages, to weigh gold, silver and other precious metals. Avoirdupois ounces and pounds were the names given to the weighing of other goods such as sugar, salt, dyes and grain.

Ghana became a republic in 1960 with Kwame Nkrumah as president. Gold commemorative coins were struck to mark this important occasion, below right, as they have been to pay tribute to significant events and leaders down the ages.

Today, the term "avoirdupois" has generally been dropped from ounces and pounds but gold is still measured in troy ounces. A troy ounce is heavier than an ordinary ounce and is equivalent to 31.103 g (1.09 oz). A troy pound contains 12 ounces, while the imperial, or avoirdupois, pound has 16 ounces. Troy weight derives its name from the city of Troyes in the Champagne region of northeastern France, which was the site of one of the largest medieval fairs in Europe. By the 16th century there was a strong alliance between Scotland and France through the marriage of Mary, Queen of Scots, to Francis II of France. As a result Scotland assumed the French weights and measures systems, which were soon passed on to England. The troy weight system was adopted by the US Mint for the regulation of coinage in 1828 and was eventually accepted throughout the world as the weight system for gold.

THE COLOUR OF GOLD

Great efforts are often made to refine the naturally alloyed gold which is recovered from the earth, and to separate its component parts. Carefully controlled alloying is also used to make gold harder so that it is suitable for a variety of uses, and in order to alter its colour. The colours created in this way vary depending on the metal or metals that are mixed in with the gold and the proportion of each. Copper tends to make gold red; silver, depending on the quantity present, imparts a green, yellow or even whitish colour. A little zinc is sometimes added to improve the appearance of alloys which have relatively small amounts of gold in them. Nickel, zinc and copper in varying proportions and combinations can also be used to produce "white gold", as can the addition of palladium. Gold of different colours has sometimes been used in combination by specialist goldsmiths to create works in which the contrasting hues are used to "paint" pictures or scenes. So high is the reflectivity of

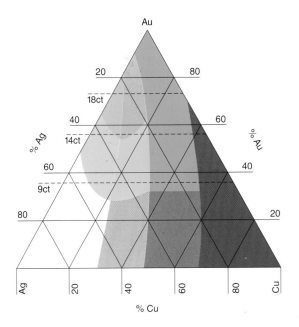

Variations in the colour of gold arise when it is alloyed with other metals. The colour triangle maps out the changes in the colour of gold (Au) achieved by the addition of different percentages of silver (Ag) and copper (Cu). For example, 18-karat gold consists of 75 percent gold and 25 percent silver and copper in varying amounts. The colour of 18-karat gold will be paler if there is more silver than copper in the alloy or more red if there is more copper than silver.

polished metal that even slight differences of colour have a striking effect.

GOLD IN THE SPACE AGE

To our eyes gold looks a rich yellow colour because of the way it reflects light. There is a rapid rise in its reflectivity in about the middle of our visual range, which is around the yellow-red area of the spectrum as opposed to the blue-green. It is also extremely efficient at reflecting infra-red radiation, almost 98.5 percent of the infra-red which falls on the metal is reflected away. In this respect gold is very slightly inferior to newly polished silver which reflects even more of this type of radiation. Gold, however, has an advantage: while silver will tarnish and darken very quickly, gold remains unaltered.

In recent decades, this fact has opened up a vast range of new uses for gold. A lot of space equipment is given a reflective coating of gold to protect it. The space helmet visors worn on the moon by US astronauts were treated in this way. The extraordinary reflective power of gold is also used to deflect and confuse the signals of heat-seeking missiles. The US president's aeroplane, Air Force One, is one of the aircraft protected by gold anti-missile reflectors. Gold also plays a vital role in astronomy because of its ability to reflect infra-red light. Gold is used in the reflective mirrors in the telescope at the Keck Observatory, Hawaii, the largest twin telescope in the world.

Methods have been found to fix very thin layers of gold to sheets of glass. These are used to clad buildings, allowing light to pass into them but preventing the sun from warming up their interiors. Equally, in winter months, the gold film on the glass helps cut heat losses. A thin film of gold, deposited on glass in a vacuum with an intermediate bismuth oxide layer, allows light through but also permits the metals to be heated up to keep the glass free of condensation or ice. Such windows are used for the windscreens of aircraft, boats and vehicles operating in extreme conditions.

Gold is also applied to a number of metal surfaces to serve as a heat shield within jet engines. In many situations it has the additional advantage that, being chemically inert, it resists the attack of oils, hydraulic fluid or jet fuel and so protects the metal on which it is deposited.

Space technology makes frequent use of gold. The helmet visors worn by US astronauts for their space walks were treated with a reflective coating of gold for protection.

Gold is an excellent conductor of electricity and an unreactive metal, which makes it suitable for computer parts such as the microprocessor, right.

The high electrical conductivity of gold, coupled with its great resistance to corrosion, makes it especially suitable for providing electrical contacts in machinery that must operate in poor conditions or in places where servicing is difficult, impossible or undesirable. Gold-plated contacts in expensive hi-fi sets are not just a matter of fashion. The metal improves the performance of the equipment and prevents the slow deterioration that occurs when contacts are made from other metals.

Gold has other contemporary uses. For a long time it was used in dentistry to make caps, fillings and bridgework and this practice still continues in some countries today. The metal is particularly suitable because it does not corrode or tarnish, but it is usually used in an alloyed form to ensure it is hard enough to take the high pressures exerted on teeth during chewing and biting. Gold is also used to colour fine china and in both colouring and decorating glass. One part gold dissolved in 50,000 parts glass produces a deep ruby colour; smaller quantities of the metal produce glass of progressively paler red colours. The uses of this noble metal will surely be even more widespread in future.

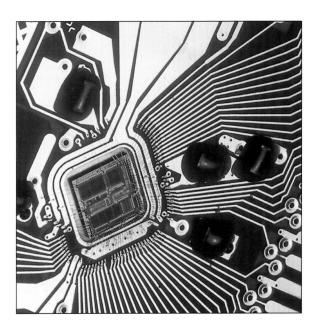

GOLD FEVER

"Many are men of wealth, and others have barely enough money to pay their way, but all are led on in the mad rush for gold by visions of untold riches and dreams of a happy age spent in ease and luxury."

The hunger for gold has driven explorers all over the world to conquer new lands. Gold was among the things Columbus was seeking when he voyaged westwards and it provided a powerful motive for the Spanish conquistadors who followed in his tracks in the 16th century. Whenever the conquistadors reached a new area they began to search for gold – and gold they found. In Mexico, the defeated Aztec king Montezuma gave conquistador Hernán Cortés a golden sun the size of a cartwheel as well as numerous animals made of gold.

Within a few years the Spanish in South America had begun to seize vast quantities of gold, often using torture to extract information about gold deposits or caches of gold objects. The Spanish conquest of the Americas was achieved by small numbers of desperate men. By bravery, deceit and treachery they were able to defeat the vastly larger armies of indigenous peoples and establish Spanish rule. The conquistadors were driven by a thirst for glory – and a hunger for gold.

THE BOUNTY OF THE INCAS

At the end of 1532 the Spanish, under the leadership of Francisco Pisarro, captured the Inca ruler Atahualpa. From his military headquarters they seized about 365 kg (800 lb) of gold. The quantity of gold surprised them and inflamed their cupidity but they were astounded by the offer that Atahualpa then made. He promised to fill a room that measured 7 x 5 m (23 x 17 ft) to about the height of 2.5 m (8 ft) with gold objects – and to do this within two months – if they would quit his kingdom.

"The largest nugget in the world" was not really a nugget, *since it was discovered underground; nor was it pure gold, although it did contain more than 55 kg (120 lb) of the precious metal. It was found in Australia in 1872.*

Within a short time the gold began to arrive: here was undeniable proof that the land offered almost limitless bounty. Needless to say, they did not leave. When the Spanish melted down the metal they had received it came to 6,000 kg (over 13,000 lb). Yet even this was not enough for them, the more they got, the

more they wanted. The gold could not come in quickly enough to satisfy their ever-growing appetites. They set about looting gold wherever they could find it.

The great Temple of the Sun at Cuzco was sacked and in a short time they had stripped 700 gold plates, each weighing about 2 kg (4.5 lb), from its structure. They also removed numerous gold effigies – one in the form of a woman weighed about 29 kg (65 lb), another, depicting a llama, weighed 26 kg (58 lb). The temple had, they reported in amazement, "a band of

"The reef, which is all auriferous, has its full width shown in the picture; it gives you an idea of the gigantic formations with which we have to deal." (John Daw's Report, 1902.)

gold eight inches wide running round the entire building at roof height" and it contained a number of vessels made half of pottery, half of gold.

TREASURES IN THE MELTING POT

A sacred garden was composed of plants made of gold and silver where the maize, for example, had

silver stems and ears of gold. The wonders of this Inca metalwork, perhaps created and treasured over several centuries, had little impact on the Spanish looters. They were after the metal itself and everything was soon melted down and turned into bars of bullion.

As they spread out through the Americas, the Spanish soldiers and settlers continued to loot and pillage towns and then set both the local population and imported slaves to mine for them. Meanwhile, the wealth of gold and silver they were acquiring attracted the attention of equally gold-hungry men from other nations. Almost as soon as they began to ship gold back to Spain attempts were made to take it by force; others thought they had every right to steal what the Spanish had already stolen. Raids on treasure vessels grew and vast fortunes were made in a matter of days.

THE FEVER FOR PIRACY

By the mid-16th century it had become necessary for Spain to organize its shipments to and from the New World into vast fleets so that they could have the benefit of heavily armed escorts. The collecting point for outgoing cargoes was Cartagena. Cargoes from western South America were brought to the isthmus of Panama by ship and then carried to the city by mule. Periodically, great fairs were held at Porto Bello from where incoming goods were distributed to virtually the whole of the Americas. Concentrating trade on the isthmus meant that great quantities of gold, silver and other goods were accumulated there, awaiting the departure for Spain. It also meant that those who preyed on this wealth knew more or less when and where it was to be shipped. Both the towns of the isthmus and the great treasure fleets were tempting targets.

The English, at war with Spain, had no compunction in attempting to seize Spanish gold. The great cities offered an almost irresistible temptation to their sea captains and some made vast sums by looting them. In 1585, Sir Francis Drake organized a highly successful major expedition, first plundering Santo Domingo and then attacking and capturing Cartagena. He held the city for six weeks and only then agreed to leave it for a ransom of 110,000 ducats. The French were also among the nations who looted and ransomed towns. In 1554, about 300 French privateers seized the town of St Jago de Cuba, held it for 30 days and took 80,000 pieces-of-eight as plunder. The next year Havana was occupied, most of the city razed and huge amounts of gold removed. Piracy in the Caribbean and in the Americas continued as a profitable venture, and Spanish gold and silver went on being "liberated" in these ways. Eventually realignments among the European powers meant that towards the end of the 17th century, raids on Spanish vessels generally became more and more a matter of private criminal enterprise rather than semi-official government policy.

The great gold discoveries of the Americas helped fuel the growth and expansion of Europe, but in the 19th century a new outbreak of gold fever spread around the world with amazing speed and the production of gold rose at an unprecedented rate. It has been estimated that six times more gold was mined in the last half of the 19th century than in the whole of the preceding century.

THE GOLD RUSHES

The great gold discoveries of the 19th century were unlike any seen before. The huge numbers that rushed to newly discovered goldfields, the vast distances they journeyed, and the new methods of mine ownership were the result of four emerging forces: new mechanisms by which information about the initial gold discoveries was spread around the world and publicized in a matter of weeks; new methods of mass transportation; a new sense of

freedom that enabled people to leave their homes and jobs and to venture out on their own and, as always, the dream of unbelievable riches from gold.

For most people, the gold rush started as an alluring combination of adventure and a belief that they could not fail to become rich. The first of these unprecedented events, and the one that set the pattern for all subsequent ones, was the Californian rush of 1848 and 1849. Gold was first discovered in California late in January 1848, during the building of a saw mill, now known as Sutter's Mill. Initially, local people were cautious about the rumoured discovery but three months later newspaper editors were beginning to print stories about the finds. A feverish interest in gold mining began to infect the locals and many left their jobs to look for gold. News of the finds spread to Hawaii and from there it spread out along the shipping lines. Via these and a number of other routes, the news spread right around the world.

THE RUSH IS ON

By June 1848, six months after the initial find, two-thirds of San Francisco's population had left to seek gold. Sailors deserted their ships as soon as they came to port and US soldiers stationed in California left their posts to seek their fortunes. By August and September 40 or more newspapers across the United States were carrying stories of gold finds and the fortunes that could be made in California. Gold fever gripped the nation.

In North America, there was a boom in sales of gold-finding devices as well as guidebooks and

Many gold mines were developed along river banks in Ghana. This is the Essamen gold mine, one of many on the Ankobra River. Another gold-bearing river is the Pra.

instruction manuals on how to locate and dig for gold. There were also similar sales in Paris, London and other major European cities. "Argonauts" became the popular term for the new generation of gold seekers who were setting off in large numbers for the almost unknown California.

Tales of the huge sums that could be made spread like wildfire through many societies around the world. Newspaper after newspaper eagerly printed accounts of vast finds. Popular writers claimed, often falsely, to have first-hand knowledge of the goldfields. One claimed that Californian river beds contained gold deposits "to the thickness of a hand". Another told of finds of 16 kg (35 lb) of gold in a single day.

In this almost hysterical atmosphere few of those who set off for California seem to have had any doubt that they would be successful. The great problem they faced, however, was getting there and getting there quickly, before all the best mining sites were taken. Despite all the difficulties and the sheer

cost of the journey, thousands of people did manage to reach California and set about prospecting for gold. By the end of 1849 perhaps as many as 50,000 were involved in mining. The number more than doubled by 1852. They came from all over the world: Europe, Chile, Australia, the Pacific Islands, and at one time, one in five miners was of Chinese origin.

THE FEVER SPREADS "DOWN UNDER"

In spite of the hazards – sickness, death, misery and failure – many did find gold. Together, individual efforts produced huge amounts of it. Between 1848 and 1853 a quarter of a million men, often working alone, extracted gold worth $200 million. Perhaps the most important effect of the events of 1848–49 was that people became used to the idea that it was possible to give up their existing life, travel half way around the globe and have as good a chance as any of making a fortune and bettering their lives.

One of the prospectors who had tried and failed to make his fortune in California was an Australian called E.H. Hargreaves. Hargreaves returned home, believing that he could find gold there. Within a very short time, in February 1851, near Bathurst, New South Wales, he succeeded. Within a year 150,000 people were involved in mining and in 1852 the state of New South Wales produced 850,000 oz of gold. In the same year, the first gold seekers arrived – between 1851 and 1861 half a million people from Great Britain alone left for Australia. The government, delighted by this sudden rise in population, rewarded Hargreaves for his discovery.

Gold fever in the rival city of Melbourne raged so fiercely that at one point only one policeman was left in the city – all the others had gone to Bathurst to dig for gold. The Melbourne civic authorities, seeing their citizens leaving in droves to seek their fortunes elsewhere, tried to reverse the trend. They offered a reward to anybody who found gold within 320 km (200 miles) of the city. Success was almost

Hargreaves discovers gold in his home country, Australia. For the first lucky arrivals there were rich pickings of nuggets, flakes and dust to be had in the highly concentrated desposits in river beds and streams.

immediate: gold was discovered at Ballarat, Victoria, and people began to pour in. Within ten years Melbourne's population had grown from 25,000 to 190,000 inhabitants and in the decade following the gold discoveries the country's population tripled.

THE KLONDIKE

The last great gold rush occurred in the far north of America near the Klondike. Today, the Klondike gold rush is remembered less for its goldfinds than for the horrific conditions suffered by those who

THE GOLD COAST CHAMBER OF MINES.

NO. OF CERTIFICATE
20

NUMBER OF SHARES
25

THE GOLD COAST CHAMBER OF MINES.

(Incorporated under the Companies Ordinance (Cap. 149)
Gold Coast Colony.)

CAPITAL - - £1,000,

Divided into 800 "A" Ordinary Shares of £1 each and 200 "B" Ordinary Shares of £1 each.

This is to Certify that Ashanti Goldfields Corporation Limited

of Obuasi, Ashanti West Africa, and 6 Southampton Street, London W.C.1.

is the Registered Holder of Twenty five —————————— "A" Ordinary Shares of

One Pound each, fully paid, numbered Threehundred thirty two to Threehundred fifty six in

THE GOLD COAST CHAMBER OF MINES, subject to the Memorandum and Articles of

Association of the Chamber.

Given under the Common Seal of the Chamber,

the 12ᵗʰ day of June, 1935.

_____ , ACTING SECRETARY.

PRESIDENT.
VICE-PRESIDENT.

NOTE.—NO TRANSFER OF ANY OF THE SHARES COMPRISED IN THIS CERTIFICATE CAN BE RECOGNISED UNTIL THE CERTIFICATE HAS BEEN DELIVERED AT THE CHAMBER'S OFFICE.

THE
COAST CHAMBER
OF MINES.

...lled and forfeited
...solution phased at
...xtraordinary General
...ting held on 14/1/64
....

...shanti Goldfields
...orporation Ltd
...Southampton Street
...Holborn. W.C.1.

Obuasi. Ashanti

25 Fully paid Shares 'A'
Ordinary N°S
332/356
by S. M. O. Barclay

12ᵗʰ June, 1935.

---

struggled to get there. It has been calculated that only about half of those who set out for the new goldfields reached them. Subzero temperatures, the icy hell of ascending the Chilkoot Pass, avalanches, disease, accidents and murder all took their toll.

The first gold in the area was discovered at Rabbit Creek (renamed Bonanza) in August 1896. In the spring of 1897 – at about the same time as the Ashanti Goldfields Corporation story started – the first successful fortune seekers went south with their new-found fortunes. Almost at once the rush began, helped by feverish newspaper publicity – editors had long realized that gold discoveries sold newspapers by the thousands. Within about ten days of the news getting out, 1,500 people had left Seattle for the north.

Mining licences were just the beginning of organized gold mining. Within about 50 years of the first gold rush, mining companies had been well established and even floated on the stock market.

From Seattle, the gold seeker could sail up to Alaska, take the trail over the Chilkoot Pass, cross the Canadian border at the top and then go by boat down the Yukon. The Chilkoot Pass, 6 km (4 miles) from bottom to top, was a dreadful place. Most prospectors had to make several trips up and down a narrow track to get their equipment and supplies to the border. Some fell and injured themselves, others were struck by out-of-control sleds or baggage; frostbite and malnutrition were additional dangers. Once at the top, prospectors had to clear Canadian

customs and could possibly be charged duty on equipment and supplies. At other times, they could be turned away at gun point if they did not have a year's supply of food that would give them a chance of survival. The trip down the Yukon was also risky, there were rocks and rapids, and the constant danger of being swamped or capsizing.

THE FEVER BREAKS

Yet, despite all these dangers and obstacles, many reached the goldfields and some even found wealth. Dawson, in the Yukon Territory, Canada, grew from a town of 500 people in 1896 to a city of 30,000 two years later. Miners swaggered about the place with pokes full of gold dust with which they paid hugely inflated prices for food, drink and entertainment. However, the boom ended almost as soon as it had begun. By 1900, the day of the claim-staking prospector was almost done and the only way to extract gold from the frozen ground was by large investment in industrial mining. The dredger took over from the shovel and the pan, and in most parts of the world the brief half-century of freedom and opportunity had ended.

Until the 1980s it appeared that gold rushes were a thing of the past. Today, most modern gold mining requires a huge investment and governments normally control access to gold resources. Yet in Brazil in 1980, an old-fashioned gold rush began.

THE BRAZILIAN BONANZA

When gold was noticed in a stream at Serra Pellada (Bald Mountain) it took only one week for 1,000 people to swarm into the area to seek their fortunes; within the space of one month there were 22,000

Indigenous Ghanaian gold seekers, right, known as galamsey, *continue to prospect independently of the large gold mining companies. Early in the 20th century, West Africa was subjected to the equivalent of the Californian gold rush, the "jungle rush". This gold boom petered out during the First World War, revived for a while after it, but collapsed again after the Second World War, when gold mining reached a point of near stagnation.*

For many of the miners in Brazil, below, discovering substantial amounts of gold is their only chance to escape from total poverty.

prospectors at work. As in other gold rushes, stories of huge finds spread rapidly. Nuggets of 3–4 kg (6–8 lb), even one of an amazing 62.1 kg (137 lb), were reported. Since then, the Brazilian gold rush has grown as other gold-bearing areas have been discovered in the Amazon and central regions. Today, there may be as many as half a million prospectors, some of them little more than children, working claims as small as 10 sq m (108 sq feet).

Gold fever is not just caused by nuggets and gold dust. Gold that was worked on years ago still arouses greed and provides a living for those who can find it, even if it is strictly illegal. Today, all over Central and South America skilled professionals are robbing graves of their gold artefacts. Some of these *guaqeros* merely trail behind archaeologists, wait till they identify a promising site and then plunder it. Sheer greed on the part of collectors and dealers has opened the way to other areas of crookedness and deception, which include smuggling and making fake gold objects, said to have been stolen from pillaged graves.

FINDING GOLD

Although the origins of gold lie deep inside the earth, the forces of nature bring it to the surface and release it to sparkle within the sludge and sands of streams and rivers. Men and women pan, sluice and dredge for easy riches yet have never found enough, and the search to find gold spreads across the world – and ever deeper into the earth.

FINDING GOLD

"Get gold humanely if possible, but at all costs, get gold"
(King Ferdinand of Spain's instruction to the conquistadors, 1511)

One of the most distinctive properties of gold is that it exists as native metal, which means that it can be found in the earth in the form of crystals, nuggets, dust or flakes, or as a thin streak held within a vein of hard, glittering quartz. This must have first attracted human interest because the metal was easy to see and it could be obtained directly, without any need to smelt and refine it. Yet easily won gold has never been enough. The history of gold finding is a history of men and women travelling vast distances across the world to seek out this precious metal, inventing ways to extract more and more gold from places where it is present in such minute quantities that it cannot be detected with the naked eye.

The primary source of "free" gold is veins of quartz. The metal in the quartz, originating deep in the central magma of the earth has, over time, been carried up towards its surface by hydrothermal solutions influenced by the movements of the seven tectonic plates that make up the lithosphere, the 145-km (90-mile) deep outer part of the earth's crust.

Rocks that contain gold eventually break down and wear away under the relentless action of water, wind and the natural rise and fall of temperature. Over millions of years, these natural forces slowly free the metal from its surrounding rock. The gold as well as the debris from the weathered rock is then washed away. This is how the most easily exploited sources of gold, called placer deposits, are created.

PLACER DEPOSITS

The primary force in carrying the gold away and depositing it in placer accumulations is water. It helps break up and erode the gold-bearing rock, especially when it penetrates the tiniest cracks and expands during freezing. Water also washes debris downhill and when it enters streams and rivers flowing water slowly separates the metal from lighter materials, such as fine grains of quartz, and allows the gold to settle in concentrated masses.

The existence of alluvial placers, those created by the action of water, relies on the fact that gold is an extremely heavy metal and will sink to the bottom of a stream quicker than lighter materials such as pebbles or grains of quartz. As the speed of running water increases or decreases, so does its capacity to bear material along. When it slows down over shallows or as its bed widens out, the heavier material will drift to the bottom. If a stream flows over beds of rock with ridges, then the metal will be trapped in the lower areas between the ridges. Even today, this sort of formation is deliberately mimicked in many of the gold-extracting devices used in modern mining.

The speed and depth of any stream, the rise and fall of the landscape through which it flows, the mixture of materials it carries, the seasonal changes in the rainfall and the rocks or silt of its bed – all these factors will influence the distribution and mass

Although gold occurs naturally as nuggets, a find as big as this one (held by Sam Jonah) is rare: gold is so soft that nuggets are usually worn down to a smaller size by the surrounding earth.

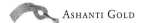

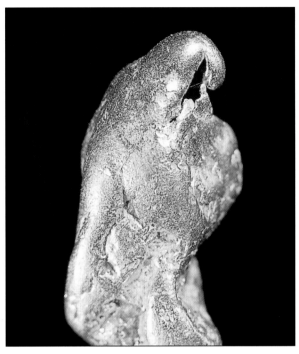

The shape of gold is affected by weathering. A prospector who finds in his pan one or more sharp-edged pieces, such as the one above, will be delighted, as it suggests that the source of gold cannot be far up stream.

A piece of gold may start its journey in a sharp-edged crystalline form, but the farther it travels and the more it is tossed and tumbled in water, the more the metal will be worn away and reduced to a smooth lump or nugget.

of the particles of gold which eventually form placer deposits. These forces will also affect the shape of the gold. A piece of gold may start its journey in a sharp-edged crystalline form, but the farther it is transported and the more it is tossed and tumbled, the more the metal will be worn away and reduced to a smooth lump or nugget.

Streams and rivers change their courses over time. As a result, alluvial placer deposits may end up many kilometres away from the river that produced them. Lakes and rivers can slowly cease to exist over thousands of years, even though the gold deposited in them remains unchanged. Over millions of years of geological activity this gold and its surrounding material may harden into a more or less solid mass. They may become compacted and the way they lie become altered by further earth movements.

The huge gold reserves of South Africa's Witswatersrand fields show an extreme form of this sort of change. About two and a half billion years ago, gold and fragments of gold-bearing rock were washed down from the hills which surrounded a great inland sea, about the size of the Caspian. Over millions of years, the material eroding into this inland sea eventually reached a thickness of about 7,600 m (25,000 ft). Further geological changes then occurred. The flat layers that were once the bottom of the sea buckled and crumpled as the earth shifted, and the layers of gold-bearing rock tilted and twisted into complex patterns. What had begun as the debris of weathered hills formed into a hard conglomerate of quartz and gold, a few centimetres to one metre thick, a seam or reef, which miners follow as it snakes through the earth, far beneath its surface.

IN THE PAN

One of the simplest ways to extract gold from rivers, streams and placer deposits is panning, a technique that has been used for thousands of years. Panning works because it relies on the same basic principle that created placer deposits: the fact that gold is heavy and that moving water can carry it less distance than it can carry lighter materials. To pan, gold-bearing earth is put into a shallow, flat-bottomed dish and swirled around with water. The lighter particles of soil and sand are gradually whirled over the edge of the vessel and the heavier particles of gold are left behind. Over the last few centuries, this method of finding gold has been used from California to West Africa, from deep in the Arctic to the rivers of South Africa. It is ideal for the single

gold worker as all it requires is a minimal amount of equipment, water, gold-bearing material, hard work – and hope.

A more advanced form of panning was a simple mechanism called the rocker or cradle. This device, as the name implies, rocked crushed gold-bearing ore backwards and forwards so water could float away the lighter materials. This allowed three or four miners, working together, to process in one day a far greater volume of gold-bearing sand and gravel than they could have done by panning individually.

Gold-bearing material was distributed on to the surface of a perforated metal plate. The finer material fell through the holes and was washed by water along the bottom as it was rocked like a cradle. The gold particles were caught in low ridges or "riffles", running at right angles to the water flow from which they were periodically removed. Modern versions of this simple mechanism continue to be in use with automatically fed and mechanically powered rocking tables covered with coarse corduroy "blankets", with pronounced ridges and channels, to trap the gold.

DEVELOPMENTS ON THE GOLDFIELDS

In the Californian goldfields, a further refinement of the pan and rocker/cradle approach was invented shortly after the great rush of 1848–49. This was the long tom, a device which could handle far more gold-bearing earth than the rocker. The long tom was an inclined trough, perhaps 7.5 m (25 ft) long, about 45 cm (18 in) wide at the top and about twice that at the bottom. The rock and sand to be treated were put in at the top and then carried down to the bottom by a stream of water fed into it by one of a team of operators. Again, the gold was caught in

Panning for gold *requires little equipment. People who use this technique usually have a whole range of pans, which they use in decreasing size. This enables them to handle less and less matter as they search their pans for the glint of gold.*

riffles at the base of the long tom and the water and waste flowed away from the open bottom.

The sluice was yet a further development of the panning procedure. Sluices were very long troughs, stretching for many metres down a hillside. Gold-bearing material and water were fed in at the top and, as the material was sluiced down, workers at the side would take out any debris, stir up the mixture to dissolve away silt and clay, or add more water or material as necessary. Once again, the heavier metal was trapped by gravity against riffles. Sluices are still used in many modern mines to catch the large pieces of gold before more complex and expensive extraction techniques are applied to the remaining material.

Another major Californian invention was the use of hydraulic power, by way of pressure hoses, to loosen and move earth that either contained gold or was blocking the way to it. Invented in 1853, the technique made use of the natural presence of water sources above the gold workings. Water was fed down channels, then through increasingly narrow tubes and finally into a flexible hose. The force of gravity and the steadily increasing narrowness of the tubes ensured that the water came out of the hose nozzle as a high-pressure jet. When this was

directed at the surface being worked, it not only broke it up but also carried the material down towards the sluices where the gold could be separated.

Digging up placer deposits is easy compared to deep mining, especially if the placer has not turned into a fairly hard mass over hundreds of thousands of years. Yet digging out gold-bearing sands and gravels using only hand tools was tough work, and the amount any one miner could extract for processing was severely limited. Sometimes the work was dangerous as well as hard: tunnels cut into relatively soft placer deposits could collapse and the pits and shafts could flood.

DREDGING THE WATERS

An industrialized form of panning, albeit a highly mechanized one, dredging works on a much larger scale than any human panner could ever hope to achieve. Gold dredgers were developed out of the vessels invented to keep rivers and harbours free of silt and work in much the same way. Water containing alluvial gold, sand and gravel is scraped or sucked up into a boat as it floats in a gold-bearing river or lake. Inside the vessel the gold is separated from the non-valuable material and the latter is discarded.

By the 1900s dredging was the most widely used method of mining placer deposits, spreading out from New Zealand, where it was first made practical, to California and many other parts of the world. It is still used extensively in the former Soviet Union. Dredging is also used today to recover gold in Ghana, and dredgers working along the Birim River not only recover gold

but also the brass vessels, pottery and stone chisels used by earlier, indigenous miners who worked the very same placer deposits hundreds of years ago.

The George Cappendell Shaft is one of the modern shafts at Obuasi lined with reinforced concrete. Earlier shafts, lined with timber, were much less safe.

MODERN MINING

While mining placer deposits remains important to world production of gold, much of the metal is now extracted by highly industrialized hard rock mining operations. Hard rock mining has come about for several reasons. The first is our increased ability to locate gold deep under the ground, in some cases thousands of metres beneath the earth's surface. Second, once we know that the metal is there, we can estimate the richness of any ore and then balance the costs of extracting and refining it against the monetary value of the gold. No modern mine can begin operations until complex and detailed calculations of its viability have been made, a far cry from the early days of mining, when a few people could decide to go down to the local river to try their luck at panning its sands.

Third, mine-engineering skills now exist to allow miners to drill and tunnel deep into the earth – so deep that the rock is hot to the touch – and, working there, cut out the ore and transport it in vast quantities to the surface. Finally, modern extraction techniques ensure that even tiny amounts of gold contained in vast masses of ore can be extracted and refined to a metal of a very high degree of purity. Several tonnes of ore may have to be dug out to produce an ounce of gold, but because the metal is so precious and the costs and profits of mining so carefully calculated, this is an acceptable ratio of waste to metal.

No modern mine is even contemplated until information from samples taken from bore holes has been carefully analysed and exhaustive studies and mapping of the area's geology as well as every other conceivable source of information have been carefully weighed.

Hoses were first used in 1853 to break up gold-bearing rock. This method of removing rock has its uses today: here, a powerful modern jet breaks up tailings material at Obuasi.

THE DESIGN OF MODERN MINES

A deep modern mine is not that different in its basic design from the early mines dug just 6–9 m (20–30 ft) into the earth. A modern mine consists of one or more shafts or declines from which horizontal tunnels branch toward the ore body. The real difference lies in the sheer size of a modern mine and the extensive reliance on mechanical power – instead of going down 9 m (30 ft), a modern miner goes down up to 4,000 m (13,120 ft) and sends millions of tonnes of material to the surface. A modern miner breaks up rock faces with high explosives and pneumatic drills and is able to operate in high working temperatures thanks to elaborate ventilation and cooling systems.

The most basic form of modern mine consists of two initial shafts linked by a cross tunnel: one shaft allows miners rapid and safe access to the gold-bearing strata and allows rock to be hauled to the surface, the other is for ventilation and to carry the services miners need for themselves and for their machinery. In this basic model of a mine, the hot stale air from the workings is sucked up this shaft and fresh cool air is pulled down the other.

These vertical shafts allow the miners to get down to the level of the gold strata, or reefs. Once they are there, horizontal tunnels, called cross-cuts, are driven out from the shaft until they get to the reef. At this point, other shafts are driven out from them to run parallel with the source of gold. These are called drives, and those at different levels in the mine are joined by more tunnels. The ones going downwards are called wintzes and those going upwards are called raises. This honeycombing of the reef divides it into exploitable sections, allowing the miners to get to as much of it as possible in safety. The raises and the wintzes are increased in size as the payable ore is cut out along them. Areas which are created by the removal of gold-bearing ore are called stopes. These are irregular cavities whose shape is determined by

Large pieces of equipment live permanently underground and are serviced in maintenance workshops that may be 800 m (½ mile) or more below the surface. Here, workers are being trained to service a Simba drill.

how far the gold-bearing rock extends and how much can be safely removed.

WARNING: DANGER

Mining can be a dangerous business and concerns for safety are at the heart of the design and operation processes. Removing rock to make shafts and tunnels and stopes requires a full understanding of the consequences if the weight of the overburden is not to come crashing down. If ore is removed from several levels in a mine, then enough distance and rock must be left between them to make sure there is proper support for the weight of rock above each of them. Fissures in the rock, the character, strength, even the compressibility and load-bearing power of different strata, all need to be carefully studied.

Water is also a great danger. Drilling or blasting into unsuspected water-bearing strata can be disastrous, as a small influx of water can quickly turn into a torrent. Early miners also had problems with water and the Romans used systems of waterwheels to keep their mine shafts from flooding; they were also used in some medieval mines. None of these,

however, could handle one-thousandth of the volume of water removed by a single modern pump.

Non-placer mining is a matter of the extraction and crushing of quartz and other rocks which contain gold. The application of explosives to this process led to a great increase in the amount of rock a small team of miners could break up and bring to the surface. Gunpowder began to be used in mining shortly after it appeared in Europe in the 13th century and it continued to be used into the 19th century when much more powerful explosives were introduced. Initially, the most important of these was the ferociously dangerous nitro-glycerine, which could be set off by any sudden shock. It could be made safer when contained in diatomatous earth and the resulting product, dynamite, could only be made to explode by special detonators that sent a sudden shock wave into it. This made it far safer to work with as well as providing miners all over the world with an explosive many, many times more powerful than gunpowder.

The enormous power released by dynamite allowed new methods of mining to be developed. It

meant that huge quantities of rock could be removed to allow access to gold-bearing strata, and it also meant that the hardest auriferous rock could be smashed into small pieces before it was lifted to the surface for crushing and refining. What had previously been impossible tasks became everyday matters for miners equipped with dynamite.

MINE POWER

Controllable and easily available power is the key to modern mining. Vast amounts of power are needed to lower miners to the working areas of the mine, to keep it ventilated, to pump out water, to transport the ore from the mine face to the bottom of the shaft, to lift it to the surface, to crush it and to extract the gold. Modern mining could not develop until adequate power supplies were available, power supplies which could be laid on exactly where they were needed, whether it was in the frozen tundra of Alaska or in the humid rain forests of Ashanti.

The great invention which led to the Industrial Revolution, the steam engine, arose out of the needs of mine operators. James Watt's crucial invention was born from his work on a model Newcomen engine, which he had been asked to repair. This, and other early steam engines, had been developed to pump water from tin mines in Cornwall, England. Watt's creation of an efficient steam engine in 1764 meant that, for the first time ever, it was possible to install a major source of power anywhere in the world where there was fuel and water.

Steam engines contributed greatly to the development of improved and more productive mining systems – working hoisting gear and crushing machinery, driving the trains that serviced mines and carrying miners and their equipment around the

The search for new ore reserves continues: diamond drillers explore the geology of Ashanti's underground operations, recovering rock core samples from drill holes for evaluation.

globe. Nowadays, electrical power is essential, provided in some cases from the mine's own generating stations or from nearby hydro-electric installations. In other cases, power is transmitted by cable over hundreds of kilometres.

Power is also essential for drilling into rock. Throughout the 19th century, many attempts were made to develop a drill efficient and reliable enough to cut into hard rock under difficult conditions, without the need for constant servicing and repair. By the first decade of the 20th century hammer drills driven by compressed air were greatly facilitating the mining of hard rock, their blades made from newly developed, harder-wearing steels.

EXTRACTION AND REFINEMENT

Modern gold mining requires a huge investment of money. In the past, a miner working alluvial deposits needed little more than a tool for loosening the earth, a wooden pan and enough food and drink to keep going until gold was found. Now hundreds of millions of dollars must be spent on exploration, surveying and sinking shafts as deep as 4,000 m (13,120 ft) and setting up extraction machinery before a single ounce of gold is obtained.

Extracting the ore from deep beneath the earth is just the first stage towards obtaining gold. The economic success or failure of such mines depends on how large a proportion of the precious metal they can extract from the rock. One reason why such enormous expenditure is justified is the mining companies' confidence that they use processes that can extract virtually all the gold that is present in the rock they recover from their mines. Before the end of the 19th century, perhaps as little as 45 or 50 percent of the gold that was present in ore was actually recovered. Extracting a higher proportion was technically too difficult, impossible, or just not worth the time and money – time and money that could be more

profitably spent on finding easier gold. Since then, new techniques have raised the extraction rate to 90 percent or above, in some cases making it profitable to go back and re-work the discarded ore in the spoil-heaps of earlier mines.

THE ROLES OF MERCURY AND CYANIDE

Two materials are of major importance in extracting gold from rock. The first is mercury, which readily forms alloys with a number of metals, including gold. Once formed, these alloys, or amalgams, can be "undone" by heating them. Mercury has a low boiling point of 357°C (675°F) so when heat is applied to an amalgam, the mercury can be vaporized. As the mercury boils off, it leaves behind the metal with which it was alloyed and the mercury can easily be condensed and re-used. This affinity of mercury for gold is the basis of a method of gold recovery that has been used for centuries. Gold-bearing rock is pulverized, and it may then be washed with running water so that the lighter material is floated away and the heavier gold trapped, in the ridges of corduroy cloth, for example. The remaining material is then mixed with mercury to produce gold amalgam. The

amalgam is carefully boiled and the gold left behind is ready for further refinement to remove any silver, copper or palladium it may contain. Ancient Romans used this technique in their mining industry and they made sure that any ore treated in this way was finely crushed so the maximum amount of gold could be recovered.

A great advance in gold extraction was made in 1886 by three Scots: John Stewart MacArthur, and two doctor brothers called Forest. They discovered that gold will form compounds with cyanide in certain conditions, ones which are never found in nature. In their process, called the MacArthur-Forest Process, the gold-bearing ore is ground up extremely finely and then treated with a very diluted solution of sodium cyanide or calcium cyanide, with water and oxygen present. The ore and the other chemicals are mixed together in a vat and stirred to make sure that all the gold comes in contact with the cyanide. The reactions that occur between them produce

The first explosives used in mining were very volatile, and the slightest movement could set off an explosion. Today, controlled explosions are carefully planned for the safest and greatest effect.

Under AGC's reforestation programme, the Loss Control Department will ensure that a mined area such as this is revegetated by "Operation Toupee".

Tropical forest in the Obuasi area may harbour substantial gold reserves. Before mining operations commence, forward planning aims at minimizing environmental damage.

compounds from which gold is comparatively easy to liberate. The solution is treated in a vacuum to suck out the oxygen, and zinc dust is then added to precipitate the gold and any other metals, such as silver and copper, which are present. The remaining material is then washed, dried and melted in the presence of fluxes which assist the gold and silver to fuse. Any other metals are removed and the gold-silver alloy refined to remove all but a trace of the silver.

Crushing rock so that it can be treated either with mercury or cyanide to extract the gold is usually done in several stages. In the first stage, the rock is smashed into pieces about 15 cm (6 in) in diameter, then gyratory crushers reduce them to about 2 cm ($^3/_4$ in) in size. These, mixed with water, produce a coarse pulp of rock and water, which is, in turn, reduced to a fine slime in pebble mills. Many mines will use a combination of different processes to make sure they extract the maximum possible amount of gold from the ore: for example, a mechanized form of traditional washing using sluices, followed up by the mercury and cyanide processes.

GOLD MINING IN ASHANTI

"Early European attempts at mining were failures because they were based on an assumption that indigenous production methods could be improved upon. As experience showed, this was just not true."

The story of gold in Ghana, at least up until the final decade of the 19th century, was largely the story of the rise and fall of the kingdom of Ashanti. The collapse of that kingdom and its incorporation into the British Colonial system in 1896 marked a major turning point in the story, opening up the way for the introduction of new, European mining methods. A year later, in 1897, the Ashanti Goldfields Corporation (AGC) was born.

But the history of gold exploitation in the region goes back many centuries before Ashanti achieved dominance. Finding gold probably developed from haphazard collecting, perhaps from river banks, into the deliberate seeking out of new sources of gold and investing time and labour extracting it. As long-distance traders from the north were drawn into the forest zone by the lure of the metal, they would have brought with them a knowledge of more efficient and productive methods of extracting gold. And the enormous demand for gold that reached across the Sahara and Europe led to a revolution in local gold production, setting in motion profound changes in society, ultimately leading to the rise of the Ashanti Empire and the splendours of its kings and courts. Although it is not known exactly when mining for gold was first practised in the forest, it is certain that mines were being worked in the interior well before the closing decades of the 15th century.

The wheels of industry continue to turn at the Sulphide Treatment Plant at the Ashanti Goldfields. Production continues 24 hours a day.

The great kingdom of Ashanti was built largely upon the golden riches that lay beneath its soil. Gold production and the growth of centralized states in the forest region went hand in hand, and alluvial and mined gold were crucial sources of wealth and power for the new kingdoms that developed from the mid-16th century onwards. By the start of the 17th century Ashanti was beginning to establish itself as an expanding power and by the middle of the 19th century it controlled most of the area that forms present-day Ghana.

Over the last 100 years, a further revolution has taken place with the introduction of deep mining and industrial-scale gold production in the Ashanti goldfields, a development that has tied the fields more closely to the world economy. AGC today can harness the sophisticated fruits of modern high technology in its pursuit of gold, but the fabulous amounts upon which the ascendancy of the Ashanti depended were extracted by far simpler means – panning and shallow mining. The amounts of gold extracted by these two indigenous techniques, which were used right up to the early 1900s, deeply impressed Europeans who were eager to find out everything they could about local gold production and identify the places where it was extracted.

Although vast quantities of gold dust and nuggets flowed into their hands, there was never enough for the Europeans whose goal was to gain control of at least some of the gold production. Their various attempts at mining, however, were doomed to failure for a variety of reasons. One was that they flew in the

face of the obvious fact that it was not in the interest of local people and their rulers that Europeans should succeed in setting up independent ventures. In addition, most of them succumbed to malaria or other tropical diseases within two or three years of their arrival. Thus they rarely, if ever, had the manpower to engage in mining operations.

Ultimately, however, the main reason for the failure of their mining attempts was the false assumption that indigenous methods could be improved upon. In fact, local gold production methods were highly effective. Local societies had evolved suitable gold-winning techniques, they controlled the gold-bearing areas and they were able to provide the necessary labour to exploit them.

COLLAPSE OF A KINGDOM

The last three decades of the 19th century were troubled times for the Ashanti who eventually found themselves at war with the British. When the British took over Kumasi in 1874 it was a disaster of the worst kind for the Ashanti kingdom, leading to a period of civil dispute and uncertainty during which the Asantehene Kofi Karikari was destooled. Prempeh I, his successor, strove to reconsolidate the state but was seized by the British in 1896 and, with some senior chiefs and household staff, taken into exile. In the same year the Kingdom of Ashanti was incorporated into the British Colonial system. After a bitter battle over the Golden Stool, the symbol and soul of political sovereignty for the Ashanti, the proud people were defeated and their kingdom was eventually annexed to the British Crown in 1901.

The weakening of central control in Ashanti opened up the way for new European gold mining enterprises. This had already been paved to some extent by the French trader and explorer Marie Joseph Bonnat, the "father" of modern gold mining on the Gold Coast. In 1877 he became the first European to obtain a concession – at Tarkwa.

GHANA'S GEOLOGY AND MINERALS

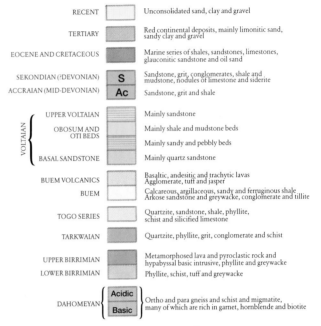

associated with the sorts of soil likely to contain gold. Earth of a blue-black or grey appearance along river beds and banks was known to lie over auriferous strata. In addition, some claimed that they could detect gold in mystical ways, such as in dreams, or by seeing a mist or glow over the place where it lay. However they did it, they were masters at finding gold.

Shallow mining was the main way of extracting gold from below the earth's immediate surface. For digging a wide variety of holes, shafts, ditches and tunnels to reach gold close to the earth's surface, the Ashanti used only the simplest of tools. The main ones were sturdy digging sticks fitted with pointed or broad-bladed iron tips, the type of tip used depending on the hardness of the material to be dug out. They were also used to break up rock. The ubiquitous all-purpose African tool, the hoe, was also widely used in mining.

In early AGC operations, adits were hand-cut into the mineral-rich hills of Obuasi, leading to work areas so confined that miners could only crawl to their tasks. The new portal at the Côte d'Or reef, at the north of the Obuasi mine, is concrete lined and large enough to allow vehicles to reach the rock face.

Trenches were also dug when there were exploitable gold resources near the surface. Such trenches, about 3 m (10 ft) deep and twice as wide, might continue for hundreds of metres, twisting and turning as they followed the gold until the source ran out and they were abandoned.

Some of this shallow mining was done individually or by small family groups, but where the gold was plentiful hundreds, even thousands, of people might be involved at the same site. There are accounts of as many as 4,000 people working at a

mining ditch 0.5 km (¼ mile) long. Missionaries in the 1860s remarked that sometimes villages were completely deserted since their entire population had flocked into the forest to the best gold-producing areas.

In pre-Colonial times, the method of remuneration for gold digging was a system whereby the Chief on whose land gold deposits were found was entitled to one-third of the recovered gold, lessees received one-third and the workforce the other. Where the Chief used his own slaves to win gold, he would appropriate it all himself.

SINKING A SHAFT

The usual method of shallow mining was to excavate a vertical shaft going down until the gold-bearing earth ended, until the shaft hit the water table and began to fill up, or until it became too difficult to go any deeper. In most cases, these limiting factors

Some of the components for the early industrial operations at Obuasi were produced on-site. Others had to be carried as headloads 200 kilometres (120 miles) from the coast.

meant that shafts did not go down more than 6–7.5 m (20–25 ft), although far deeper ones are occasionally recorded.

Shafts were so narrow that miners could brace themselves between their walls in the descent. Usually steps were cut into the shaft's sides to help miners climb up and down; ladders seemed to be used relatively rarely. At the bottom, the shaft opened out into a more or less circular chamber as more of the rock and soil was dug out. This was pulled up to the surface in baskets, calabashes or wooden containers tied to the end of fibre ropes. The men then ground the soil to a fine powder on a slab of granite, and the powdered ore was collected in calabashes and washed by the women in order to obtain gold.

When it became too difficult or dangerous to go any deeper, the work in one shaft was stopped and another was dug, often only a few metres away. The bases of the two shafts might eventually be joined by a horizontal tunnel. Once a shaft had been worked no attempt was made to fill it, it was simply abandoned. Even today, there are areas of the Ashanti forest that are so riddled with mine shafts dug in the 19th century that it is perilous to walk across them.

DEEP MINING

By the 19th century, some Akan gold miners were tunnelling deep into the earth, going down 30 m (100 ft) or more and then driving sideways in order to extract gold-bearing quartz. When the British started to explore the gold-producing areas of Ashanti in 1896, for example, they were astonished to find a mine that followed a reef into a hillside for 75–90 m (250–300 ft), with huge galleries, timbered throughout their length. The enormous amount of Ashanti mining activity and the huge quantities of gold it produced become even more impressive when one remembers that there were no machines or high explosives, nothing but the miners' own strength, skill and bravery.

It seems that in some mines fire was pressed into service. A fire burning at the bottom of one shaft was used to draw air down a nearby shaft connected to it by a tunnel or gallery. Fires were also lit on the quartz exposed in a shaft or gallery: once the rock had heated up cold water was dashed on it to cause it to crack and make it easier to break up.

Those working underground were exposed to other dangers: the working conditions were often hot, cramped and dark – the only source of light being small lamps burning palm oil or shea butter (one of the cheapest and most frequently used oils in Ghana). Rock falls constantly threatened, and there are several accounts of mines collapsing on miners.

Work was not only dangerous, it was also difficult. Once the rock at the mine face was broken up, it was hauled to the surface, usually in a stout

The forest settlement, below left, is typical of the Obuasi mining development at the turn of the century. Today, miners and their families live in planned estates, below right.

Modern day Obuasi, *surrounded by rolling hills, is the focus of the resurgence of gold mining in Ghana.*

basket that was fastened to a vegetable-fibre rope. Reducing the rock to powder was extremely hard work. The large irregular lumps were hit with hammers, until they broke down into more manageable pieces. These were then passed to women whose task was to grind them down to powder. This was done by rubbing the pieces to and fro between a granite roller and slab. Generally the ore was subjected to several successive crushings, perhaps as many as six or eight. After many hours of work the resulting powder was carefully collected. When a sufficient quantity had been produced it was then washed in the usual way to separate the gold from the powdered rock.

EARLY DAYS AT OBUASI

When Edwin Cade, mining engineer John Daw and 15 others finally reached Obuasi, along with the 40

tonnes of machinery they had had transported 190 km (120 miles) through malaria-infested forest, across rivers and along bush paths, they had to clear a large section of forest and reassemble their machinery. Despite innumerable difficulties, Cade was able to report in July 1898 that 262 tonnes of ore had been crushed and gold to the value of £2,665 had been recovered.

The early days of the Ashanti Goldfields Corporation were difficult. Time would show, of course, that Cade and his partners had control of a splendid concession indeed but developing it was far from easy. In order to show a profit, the more easily accessible sources of gold were worked first, but these had only a short-term potential.

At the height of its activity, the Anyinam surface mine at Obuasi, right, was a rich source of gold with low extraction costs.

The viewing point at Obuasi offers this panorama of mining activity, left.

The excavator below is preparing the ground for mining ore at the Justice open pit at Obuasi.

Production was interrupted during the Yaa Asantewaa war against the British in 1900 and it was necessary to discover far more about the complex geology of the area before developing the more difficult and expensive deep shafts.

The arrival at Obuasi of the railway line from the coast, however, allowed the easier transportation of supplies and machinery, including the winding gear and other equipment needed to take the mine to the next stage of development. New deposits of ore were identified and the production of gold began to rise. Between the years 1911 and 1931 the annual output fluctuated between a minimum of 69,000 oz and a maximum of 169,000 oz, with most years showing an output of between 80,000 and 100,000 oz. As the goldfield developed, production was concentrated on the three main lodes: "Ashanti", "Côte d'Or" and "Obuasi".

THE WORKINGS OF A MODERN MINE

AGC currently owns and operates one of the oldest, largest and richest gold mines in the world, which is located near the township of Obuasi. The mine has been in production for 100 years and in the financial year 1995–96 produced over 930,000 oz of gold. In

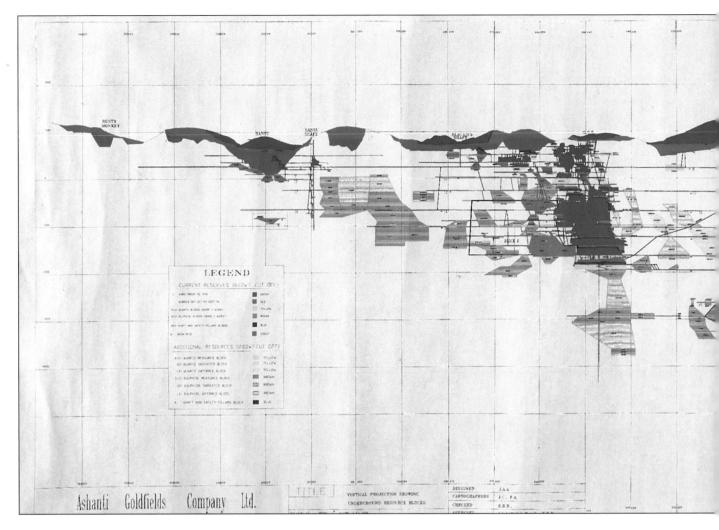

LEGEND

CURRENT RESERVES (6.00WT CUT OFF)

ADDITIONAL RESOURCES (2.60WT CUT OFF)

Ashanti Goldfields Company Ltd.

TITLE

VERTICAL PROJECTION SHOWING
UNDERGROUND RESOURCE BLOCKS

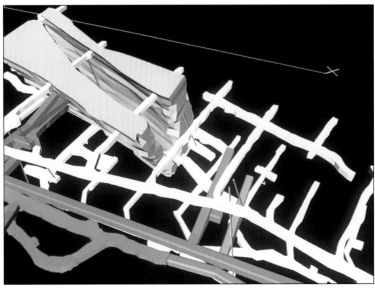

The Ashanti Goldfields Company's *Obuasi mine stretches along a remarkable 8 km (5 miles) to a depth of about 1.5 km (1 mile). Mineralization is open at depth and along strike. This 100-year-old mine still has significant exploration potential.*

The use of *three-dimensional CAD (Computer-Aided Design) techniques for geological evaluation and mining design keeps modern mining companies like the Ashanti Goldfields Company at the cutting edge and ensures the best development of mining resources.*

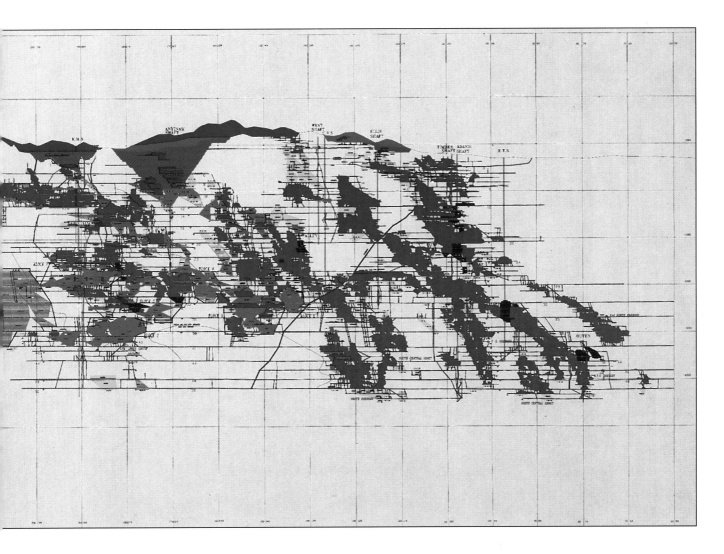

1997, its centenary year, the mine had measured and indicated resources of 21 million oz of gold within its perimeters.

The AGC mine operation at Obuasi comprises the Obuasi mine, the Sansu open-pit operation and the Pompora and Sansu processing plants as well as all the associated facilities. The mines produce both gold and minor silver in the form of doré bars, which are refined in Switzerland. The AGC mine provides over 8,000 jobs, and a further 1,000 people are employed just to search for and develop new underground activities. This is a far cry from the lone panner or group of miners collecting gold from a sluice or long tom. In a further comparison to the

past, the digging tools used in modern mining are massive and the extraction techniques much more complicated than the simple methods of the past. However, it is interesting to note that new mining techniques are based on the old ones – miners still go underground to blast away rock that must first be crushed before gold can be extracted. Today though, much time and money is spent on core sampling and analysis in order to develop operations further. In the open-pit operation, samples are taken and maps are drawn every 30 m (100 ft) and samples are then analysed for gold content. Sampling through the ore body on 60-m (200-ft) centres along the strike is the basis for exploration of underground mineralization.

OPEN-PIT MINING: THE CONCENTRIC
LINES ON THE PIT'S SURFACE MARK
THE "BENCHES" CUT THROUGH
BLASTING SO THAT THE ORE COULD
BE REMOVED LAYER BY LAYER

ACCESS ROAD FOR THE PIT

WORKINGS
AT OBUASI

Surface and underground operations take place at

Obuasi. The underground workings have been

developed along a strike length of 8 km (5 miles)

and to a depth of 1,500 m (5,000 feet). The mine

complex has more than 10 functional shafts

which, between them, every year hoist some

2 million tonnes of ore and 700,000 tonnes of

waste. The first shaft was sunk in 1907. Today

the most prominent are the Kwesi Mensah and

George Cappendell shafts. A new one,

Stonewall Shaft, will be commissioned in 1998.

A TYPICAL CUT AND FILL STOPE WITH
LOAD HAUL DUMP EQUIPMENT.

STORAGE TANKS

THE TOWN OF OBUASI

HIGH TENSILE STEEL ROPES
RUN THE PULLEY SYSTEM

HEADGEAR FOR KWESI
MENSAH SHAFT

INSIDE THE FAN HOUSE,
MASSIVE FANS DRAW AIR FROM
THE ATMOSPHERE TO
VENTILATE THE MINE

EXHAUST
AN HOUSE

HOIST ROOM HOUSING
THE HOIST MECHANISM

BLACKEE'S
VENTILATION
SHAFT

VENTILATION
EXHAUST SHAFT

TRUCKS FOR CARRYING ORE AND WASTE

AN ELECTRO-HYDRAULIC DRILL
EXTENDS A DEVELOPMENT HEADING.

CAGES CARRY WORKERS
AND MATERIALS

A SUB-VERTICAL
SHAFT HAS ITS
OWN HOISTING
SYSTEM

TUNNELS AT GREATER DEPTHS ARE
STILL BEING EXTENDED

79

1 Samples are taken from exploration areas and are tagged and marked, ready for assay preparation. Taking samples and testing them reduces the risk as well as the costs involved in mining exploration.

2 Small bowls, or cupels, are placed in an assay furnace, to determine whether there are new ore deposits or existing ore bodies for mining. Cupels are usually made from bone ash, which can withstand the high temperatures of the furnace.

3 Atomic absorption units in the assay laboratory provide the final assay results. The results will be heavily analysed and studied before any action is taken – in the days before such testing, miners relied on other methods of finding gold such as the colour of soil and the surrounding vegetation.

4 A report is made ready for despatch to the field. The assay unit processes and analyses the different types of ore not only for the Ashanti Goldfields Company but for concessions throughout west Africa. The assay laboratory uses some of the most technologically advanced processes available today.

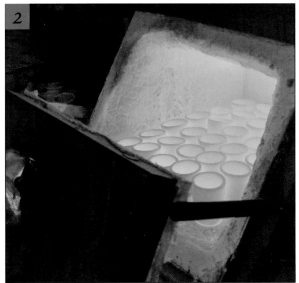

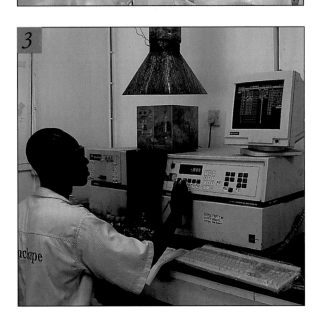

GETTING TO THE ORE

There are two kinds of mines – open-pit mines and underground mines. In the past, miners made use of both methods, just as today. In the case of open-pit mines, the rock had to be taken away to be crushed before being panned or extracted in some other way using water, making use of the fact that gold is a dense element and will sink when other matter will float. Sometimes, of course, water was diverted to the open areas where people were searching for gold-laden rock. Today, oxide and sulphide ores are mined by open-pit methods and within the open-pit mine at Obuasi, for example, there are 14 separate pits. Current production is around 8,000 tonnes of ore per day, based on a 24-hour working period. The simple shovel has been replaced by 32-tonne mechanical drive haul trucks and 400-kilowatt-powered shovels

The surface drill ring, above left, is probing into and sampling a new potential ore body. Many samples will be taken to the assay laboratory for testing and careful analysis before any mining is started.

Holes are bored with formidable machines such as the Large Diameter Raise Boring machine, above right. This machine drills and reams holes up to 5 m (16½ ft) in diameter and to depths of more than 800 m (2,625 ft).

and backhoes. Ore is taken away from the mine itself for processing – no miner in the past could possibly process the quantity of ore that is transported out of the mines today. At AGC, gold-bearing ore is also transported to its processing plants by an overground railway system, which allows millions of tonnes to be transported from mines every day.

As with open-cast mines, one of the main differences between underground mining of the past and that of the present is the scale of the operation. Modern underground mines reach incredible depths. Some of the mine shafts are as deep as 4 km (over 2 miles) – straight down into the earth – and the Obuasi strike is about 8 km (5 miles). The elevators that carry the miners down into the shaft have to be large enough to transport mining equipment, too, including huge

The twin-boom electro-hydraulic jumbo drill rig above is *positioned ready to start drilling into an underground development heading. Drills used in underground mining have to be extremely powerful.*

The group of miners on the left have various operating *assignments at a mechanized cut and fill stope, which is a steplike excavation made in a mine to extract ore.*

Not everyone working in a mine is digging for ore. In the picture on the left, for example, a surveyor is at work in an underground excavation, providing information for the miners about where to dig.

Among the safety bracings used in working tunnels are steel cables, right. Pit props are often cut from teak, a renewable plantation crop in Ghana.

From the surveyor's report, likely new ore seams will be identified. Holes are drilled in the rock face, below, and dynamite inserted. The area is then cleared for the controlled explosions that blast open the face.

The safety and personal protection of workers has become a priority since the photograph, right, was taken.

The massive diesel-powered Load Haul Dump machine, far right, is operating in a typical cut and fill stope, or working area. The broken ore will be taken to a central chute, and then out of the mine for processing.

In order to access the work face the twin-boom electro-hydraulic drill rig, below, is being moved down the Côte d'Or decline.

power drills and massive trucks. Although ventilation has improved since the old underground mining days, there is still little light in the mines, and miners work only by the small lights located on their hard hats. Explosives are still used to blast rock for crushing and processing, but today, blasting operations are more controlled and safer than in the past. They have to be when they occur kilometres under the ground. Massive moving equipment carries the ore away for processing – in one year, more than 1.2 million tonnes of ore will be hoisted up a single mine shaft and taken away for processing.

PROCESSING GOLD TODAY

In a modern working mine several extraction techniques are employed. In the past miners could only wash specks of gold out using techniques based on the fact that gold is a heavy metal and will sink while other elements are washed away. Later, other methods based on chemical bonds were developed. At AGC, these chemical techniques have been developed further so that around 90 percent of gold present in ore can be extracted. In fact, modern extraction techniques are so efficient, it is profitable for the company to re-process "tailings", the rock and soil that have already gone through one of the traditional extraction processes, extracting gold that the earlier techniques were not able to remove.

The extraction of gold at AGC is done at a number of treatment plants, some as large as a football field, extracting gold from thousands of tonnes of ore every day. These include the Pompora Treatment Plant, Tailings Treatment Plant, Oxide Treatment Plant and Sulphide Treatment Plant, as

well as the Heap Leach facility. In the past, gold production at the mine concentrated on the underground mining of narrow, high-grade quartz and sulphide veins and reefs. The ore has been treated at the Pompora Treatment Plant since 1947. The processes involve the flotation and roasting of concentrates, as well as carbon-in-leach technology. The plant is capable of treating several types of ore. The Oxide Treatment Plant uses carbon-in-leach technology and processes oxide ores from the surface mines, while the Heap Leach facility is used for processing low-grade ore.

Since 1988, AGC has been recovering gold by re-treating the tailings, which are produced as a by-product of previous mining activities. The tailings are treated at the Tailings Treatment Plant, where the recovery level of 38 percent is

AGC's growth strategy has led to new developments all over Africa. Above, international investors at the Siguiri project in Guinea. Left, the crushing plant and conveyor belt system at the Iduapriem mines in Ghana. Centre, above: international fund managers visit the Geita project in Tanzania. Centre, below: the Heap Leach project at Ayanfuri mine near Obuasi. Right, the Freda Rebecca mine is Zimbabwe's biggest gold producer.

remarkable, considering the ore had already been processed once before.

MODERN INNOVATIONS

The five processing and treatment plants also include the Sulphide Treatment Plant, which uses the BIOX® process in its operation and is much larger than any of the other plants. It is capable of treating more than five times the amount of concentrate of the largest of them, even though the individual reactor is only 50 percent larger in size. The BIOX® process is a relatively new treatment for sulphide ores, which is why there are currently only four such commercial plants in operation worldwide. BIOX® is a continuous operation using bacterial action to oxidize the sulphides into a form which can then be effectively leached by conventional cyanidation methods. It is carried out in a number of continuously stirred tank reactors under controlled conditions that are necessary to keep the bacteria alive. Treatment plants, like the mines, are worked around the clock, and the Sulphide Treatment Plant processes around 240,000 tonnes of ore per month – around 2.9 million tonnes of ore per year – which is some 19 percent higher than the original design capacity.

*Commissioned in April 1994, the Sulphide Treatment BIOX®
Plant at Obuasi, is the world's largest gold-processing facility,
utilizing bio-oxidation of sulphide concentrates to recover gold,
and operates to the highest environmental standards.*

*After dark, the same scene is lit up, above right, so that work
can continue 24 hours per day.*

*The Ashanti Goldfields Company's five processing facilities,
shown in the diagram below right, provide flexibility in
optimizing gold recovery from surface and underground ores.*

GOLD MINING AND THE ENVIRONMENT

The effect of mining on the environment has long been recognized as a major hazard to river systems and to the human environment. One obvious effect is the deforestation that is necessary for open-cast mining. Mercury is used both in modern extraction methods and by rogue individual panners called *galamsey*, who use mercury to extract gold from their pans. This is done by mixing mercury in with the sediment in the pan where it binds with gold. The resulting amalgam is heated, causing the mercury to evaporate while the gold is left behind. The handling and disposal of mercury by the *galamsey* goes

OVERVIEW OF MINING AND PROCESSING OPERATIONS

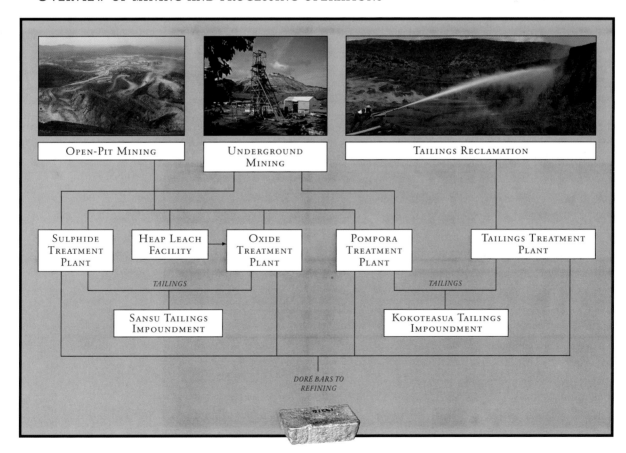

OPEN-PIT MINING	UNDERGROUND MINING	TAILINGS RECLAMATION

SULPHIDE TREATMENT PLANT	HEAP LEACH FACILITY	OXIDE TREATMENT PLANT	POMPORA TREATMENT PLANT	TAILINGS TREATMENT PLANT

TAILINGS

TAILINGS

SANSU TAILINGS IMPOUNDMENT	KOKOTEASUA TAILINGS IMPOUNDMENT

DORÉ BARS TO REFINING

unchecked and it can contaminate both soil and water as well as consituting a risk to the *galamsey*'s personal health in the form of mercury poisoning.

Throughout the history of mining the degradation of the environment at mining concessions has been taken for granted as a "natural" consequence of events in the industry. In its very early history, AGC was no exception. However, armed with knowledge of the harmful effects of deforestation and the highly toxic substances associated with gold mining, AGC has developed an environmental management programme that is

The complex technology *of the BIOX® Plant is supervised from a computer-equipped control room, far right, and can be observed from overhead walkways, above right.*

The bacterial leaching process, *below, takes place in four trains of six stainless steel tanks, right. The AGC BIOX® plant is the largest in the world.*

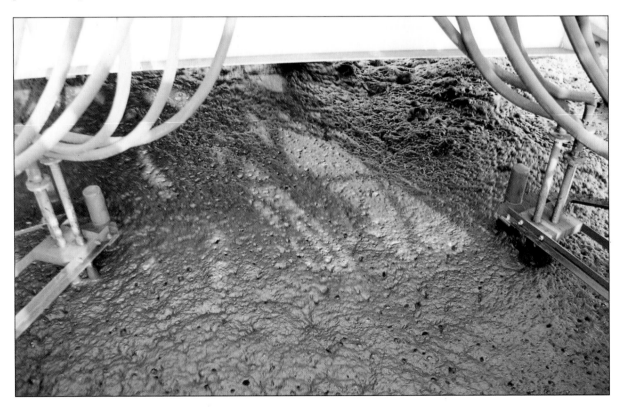

SUMMARY OF BIOX® PROCESSES

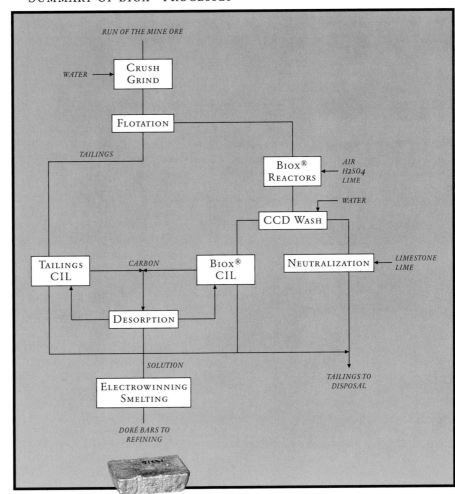

The stages of processing sulphide ores at AGC's state-of-the-art BIOX® Plant. It can handle 210,000 tonnes of ore a month in an environmentally friendly process. This is the most technologically advanced of the five different treatment processes used at the Obuasi mine.

designed to ensure that the ecology of its mining concessions is protected.

In order to ensure that it has the appropriate scientific and technological basis to pursue its environmental policy, AGC has established its own environmental department with a well-equipped laboratory to develop measures to mitigate the impact of the company's operation on the people and the environment of Obuasi and its environs.

AGC has also embarked on a programme of waste minimalization involving the recycling of its waste and the safe and proper disposal of other wastes that cannot be recycled. Finally, AGC periodically prepares environmental action plans, which involve a complete review of the environmental impact of all operations. For the

effective implementation of these plans, covering water, air, ground vibration and airblasts, samples are taken regularly.

This panoramic view of the Sulphide Treatment Plant, above, is an exhibition of the complexity of this type of gold-recovery technology in Obuasi.

Tending the revegetation experiments at AGC's field operations in Obuasi, right. Older industrial areas are currently being rehabilitated with the replanting of numerous indigenous shrubs and trees.

Air sampling equipment, far right, is used to gather data throughout the Obuasi operating area to ensure compliance with both Ghanaian and world environmental standards.

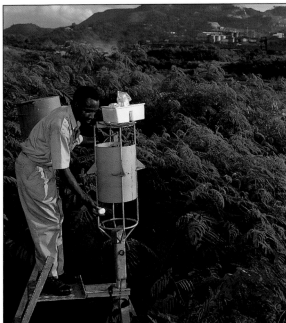

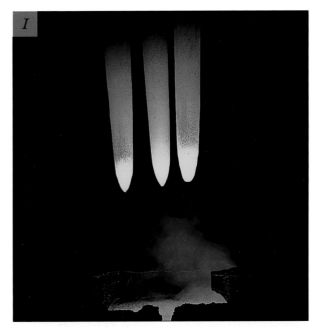

Molten gold, *left, is being poured from the ore furnace into the cascade bar moulds to form bars.*

The various stages in preparing the gold bars *for their final refinement are shown above:*
I Electrically heated prongs stir the molten gold. Here they have been lifted up so that the gold can be poured. **2** *A newly cast bar is transferred for cleaning.* **3** *Any slag that has adhered during the smelting process is removed.* **4** *The finished product is stamped, ready to be transported to the refinery.*

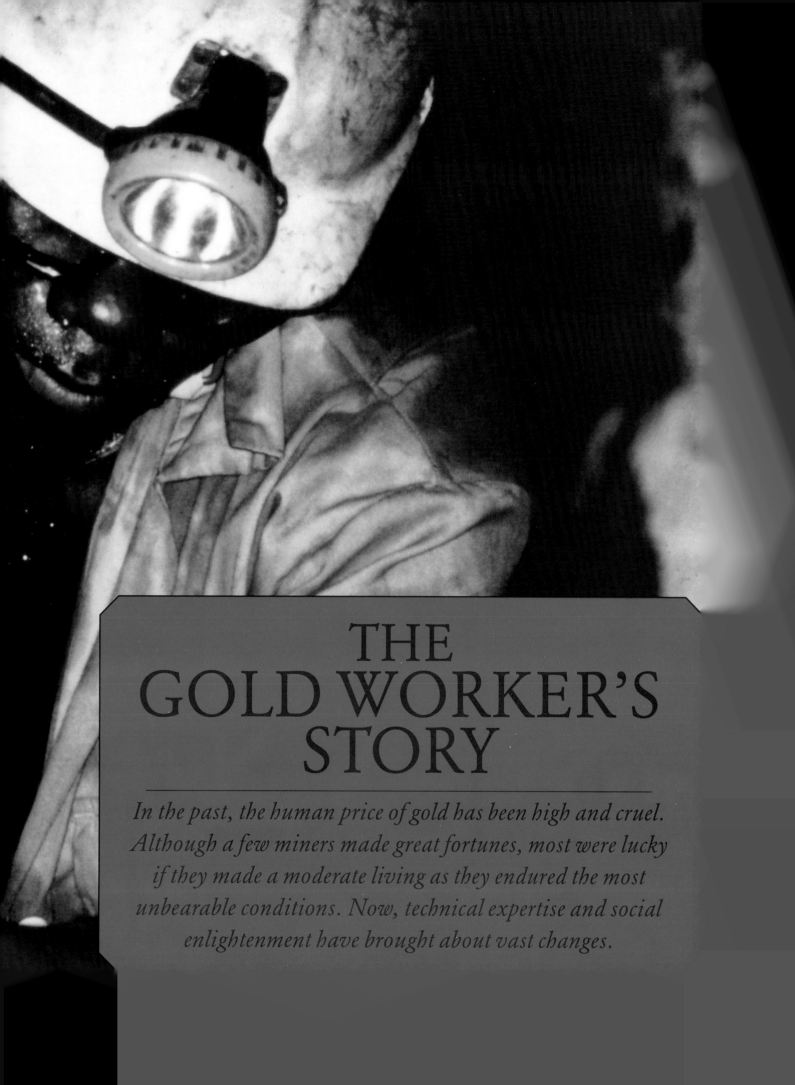

THE GOLD WORKER'S STORY

In the past, the human price of gold has been high and cruel. Although a few miners made great fortunes, most were lucky if they made a moderate living as they endured the most unbearable conditions. Now, technical expertise and social enlightenment have brought about vast changes.

THE GOLD WORKER'S STORY

"In the past conditions were often hard, sometimes dreadfully so . . . many gold miners today, even if they cannot make fortunes, are at least assured of steady wages and decent conditions."

From the slaves of pre-Classical Greece to the serfs of Siberia under the Tzars, men, women and children were forced to work in gold mines for long hours – sometimes spending a whole week underground – struggling to extract gold in difficult and dangerous conditions. The horror was often compounded by the rough treatment meted out by their overseers. Both free and unfree miners, or slaves, dug for gold in Ashanti but it is probable that, because of the Ashantis' enlightened social structure, slaves were treated more humanely than in many other societies. Clearly, though, before the advent of modern technology, the gold worker's story was generally one of more or less unalleviated misery.

As modern industrial mining has developed, progressively stricter safety and training regimes have been created and many gold miners today, even if they cannot make fortunes, are at least assured of steady wages and decent conditions. In part this is a matter of straightforward economics: modern mining depends on processing a huge amount of ore to extract a small but predictable quantity of gold from each and every tonne of it. Work on this sort of industrial scale requires highly trained and efficient miners if it is to succeed. There is another reason for the improvement of the conditions for many miners: the mines they work in are owned

Just outside the gates of the Ashanti Goldfields Company's operational headquarters at Obuasi is a statue that celebrates the gold miner's contribution to the industry in Ghana.

by the state and most states accept a duty to set minimum standards of health and safety for their workers.

THE HUMAN EFFORT

Until relatively recent times, mining relied almost entirely on human effort. Generally, it operated through brute force, occasionally through brute force directed by a degree of skill and experience. There were no machines to assist the miners, no animals that could be used to supplement their efforts and no explosives. Many of the shafts and galleries of mines were so narrow and cramped that they could only be worked by one miner at a time, who had to rely on his own unassisted strength and endurance.

In ancient Greece, as in so many other parts of the ancient world, gold mining developed from panning for gold to digging for it beneath the earth. In the pre-Classical period (before *c.* 500 BC) most gold recovered was of alluvial origin. Shaft mining was also practised, but conditions in many of the mines were dreadful. Shafts and tunnels were tiny and often there was not enough room to stand up. Ventilation was poor and little attempt seems to have been made to introduce fresh air into the mine workings except at the highly productive Athenian silver mines at Laurion. Here, some shafts were sunk in pairs and joined by galleries; fires were lit at the bottom of one shaft so that the rising heated air would draw cold air down the other. The same ventilation technique was also used in early Ashanti

underground workings. The miners had to depend on small oil lamps or torches made of resinous materials or skins soaked in oil as their only source of light underground.

The Roman Empire, as it expanded, gained control of more and more gold-producing areas. Once under Roman control, the state had the final say in how the mines were worked, setting out detailed conditions and rules on how mines should be operated, and, under Hadrian, specifying extremely harsh penalties for those who stole ore or removed the stone pillars supporting the gallery roofs. The conditions in most mines were undoubtedly bad: the Roman philosopher Lucretius speaks of illnesses in gold mines caused by poisonous fumes; roof falls were an ever-present danger, and most mines were hot, smoky and badly ventilated.

As under the Greeks, most miners were slaves although there are accounts of provincials and even soldiers being forced into service as miners. Before Christianity became accepted by the emperor Constantine, Christians too were forced to work in mines. Not only were miners slaves but in some cases they were also kept in chains. In one Roman mine a skeleton has been found with its ankles still linked by iron chains. Such was the price of gold in the ancient world.

TECHNOLOGY IN THE ANCIENT WORLD

The technology of the Romans was more advanced than that of their predecessors and there is evidence that they employed a certain amount of machinery in mining, which must have made working conditions somewhat easier. Mines usually stopped above the water table, to go deeper generally meant that the shaft could be flooded. If a shaft flooded it would be bailed out, literally, by human effort: by hauling buckets of water up on ropes. The Romans did not always rely exclusively on mere manpower: they also used waterwheels. When the Spanish

Simple, effective, cheap – and invented in the 3rd century BC – *the Archimedean screw is still used for raising water in rural communities in present-day Egypt.*

Ríotinto silver mine, which had been worked by the Romans, was reopened in the 18th century, a Roman system of stepped waterwheels was discovered. Water was lifted to successively higher levels by a series of pairs of wheels, each of which raised the water about 4 m (12 ft) to the next level. In this way, they managed to raise quantities of water about 30 m (100 ft). Some such wheels were prefabricated: one in the British Museum, England, is still marked with numbers showing how the pieces were fitted together when it was reassembled inside the mine.

The Romans and Egyptians also used Archimedean screws for raising water: these are helical screws, which run the whole length of a central shaft and revolve in a tube. When one end of the tube is slanted down into water and the screw turned, the water is propelled to the top and out. Like the waterwheels described above, these screws could be used in series: the water from the first one was emptied into a reservoir from which it was drawn up by a second, and so on. Yet, in the end, even these technical advances had to be driven by human power. The Archimedean screws had to be turned by

hand and the waterwheels were kept in motion by a person walking round and round on a narrow and uncomfortable treadmill.

THE EARLY MINERS OF SOUTH AMERICA
A similar system of compulsory mining labour was introduced by the Spanish and Portuguese into their dominions in the New World. In South America the type of mining that was practised before the Spanish Conquest was normally small scale and probably much less destructive of human life. Even so, mining

The early mining activities at AGC depended to a large extent on the influx of migrant workers from other parts of West Africa, who became part of the Obuasi community.

must have been a hard and hazardous occupation. Placer deposits were dug using wooden digging sticks and the earth carried down to the nearest stream to be panned. Occasionally, streams running in gold-bearing beds were diverted so that the sand could be exploited more easily. In some areas the indigenous people dug shafts to reach quartz veins

containing gold. Some 19th-century descriptions of far older shafts indicate they were not more than 1 m (3 ft) wide. The deepest shafts, as deep as 25 m (80ft), had steps cut in their sides. Sloping shafts, inclined at about 30°, were longer, up to 36 m (118 ft) in length and so narrow that there was no room for a person to turn round in them.

There were no side galleries in the mine shafts and no attempts to link shafts together by means of horizontal tunnels. Where gold was present in considerable quantities large numbers of vertical shafts would be dug with only a few metres of solid ground separating each of them. The number of these shafts perforating the ground suggests that in some areas large numbers of men were engaged in extracting gold. Not all miners escaped alive from their work: in the 18th and 19th centuries treasure hunters and miners came across the skeletons of miners killed in rockfalls in mining shafts.

RUTHLESS INVADERS

At least some settlements in the pre-Spanish period seem to have been specialized centres of mining and gold working. One such place was Buritica, situated in the mountains in what is now western Colombia. Here mine shafts were about 5 m (16 ft) deep dug out by slaves. According to early Spanish reports, some of the slaves were slain to provide the fat used in lamps and for eating. However, it is very difficult to know the truth of such assertions as the Spanish were extremely eager to portray local people as vile savages to justify their own cruelty and rapacity.

Almost as soon as they had established their rule, the Spanish in South America began to organize the indigenous people to mine for them, imposing a much harsher and far more ruthless system than had existed previously. It quickly became clear that all who mined for the Spanish Empire laboured under a cruel regime. Some attempts were made by the senior authorities to protect the Indians from the worst

On a payday in 1908, the paymaster's office was thronged, right. Parts of the building survive today in an administration centre which grew around them, above.

excesses of mine controllers – for example, a royal decree of 1551 said that only Indians who volunteered were to be employed in mining and some of the Spanish tried to recruit local labour to work in the mines for wages. However, these attempts proved unsuccessful. Within a short time the Spanish had established a system of labour levies from each area and later they imported African slaves to be used in mining.

In Brazil the Portuguese were initially far less successful in the hunt for gold than the Spanish had been in the New World. Then, in the 1680s and '90s, alluvial gold began to be found on the highland plateau of Sao Paulo di Piratininga. Here, too, the mines were worked by slaves controlled by local landlords, who had moved into the area to exploit the new finds. Initially, something like the gold rushes of the late 19th century seems to have occurred: people flooded into the area bringing slaves of African origin with them, and eventually driving away into the interior the local people who had been employing Amerindian slaves. In came: "all

The stamp mill and filler plant in 1905, right. Once the rail link with the coast was established in 1901, the mine developed rapidly as materials and equipment could be brought in.

Stamp mills under construction. Crushing the ore in this way was the method of extracting gold chosen by the founders of AGC.

sorts and conditions of persons; men and women; young and old; poor and rich; gentry and commoners; laymen and clergy and religious of different Orders, many of which have neither house nor convent in Brazil". The causes of this influx were similar to those of the later gold rushes: the prospect of sudden wealth.

MINING FOR THE TZARS

From the end of the 18th century to the present day Imperial Russia and its successor states have been major contributors to world gold production through one of the most important sources of gold, the Ural Mountains. The rivers and streams flowing from them were being panned thousands of years ago, and some of the gold they produced was eventually traded into the ancient Mediterranean

world. Modern gold mining in the area began in 1774 with the discovery of a gold-bearing quartz outcrop near the city of Ekaterinburg. The new mine was placed under direct royal control and, encouraged by its productivity, the Tzars instituted programmes to seek out further gold resources.

Expeditions to remote areas of Siberia revealed more goldfields. The Tzars transported whole families of serfs as well as convicts to work as miners. The conditions they endured there were terrible indeed: not only were the goldfields in remote and inhospitable regions but the mine overseers had, in effect, the power of life and death over their miners,

although corporal punishment was officially forbidden. Miners were expected to work from five o'clock in the morning until eight o'clock at night, six days per week, while those who commanded their labour and took the gold they produced lived in enormous luxury.

THE PROSPECTOR'S STORY

The Californian gold rush of 1849 was a new phenomenon. People flocked to the state from many parts of the world, driven by the belief that they could become rich. Unlike many miners in the past, the great majority of them were free, bound to nobody and at liberty to stake their claim to wealth with virtually no control by anyone else. Gold was there for the taking and success depended solely on

The first railway track was made of wood. Pairs of men would carry four 3.5-m (12-ft) lengths of rail at a time to the site – a load of almost 135 kg (300 lbs).

their own efforts and luck. Prospectors from Chile and other parts of South America who brought dependent peons to work for them were despised by the majority of miners who had absorbed the egalitarian ethos of America. In these new circumstances the gold miner's story began to take on a new shape. For many, of course, it was the same old tale: agonizing labour, sickness, near starvation – and little reward. For some who made the journey to California conditions were so harsh that they succumbed and died, for others conditions were so unbearable that, defeated, they gave up and left.

In California in 1849 there were far too few soldiers or other government officials to maintain the peace among the thousands of polyglot miners desperate to stake a claim in the best area and make their fortune. Much of the responsibility for preventing murder and mayhem, for want of any alternative, fell on the miners themselves. Under these anarchic conditions men needed new laws, new systems for the control of property, and new ways to balance greed with the need to cooperate with each other. Most interesting is the way in which miners began to create a different sort of mining society for themselves.

The scheme that eventually developed had a beautiful simplicity about it – and worked so well – that it was rapidly adopted throughout the goldfields, in more than 500 mining camps. The basic rule was this: to keep a claim, it had to be marked and worked. If a miner did not do so, the right to mine the land and to any gold it might contain was lost. This rule formed the basis for the development of law and order in the goldfields. Camps elected a claims officer whose job it was to register or record in some way each claim and to settle any disputes that arose. Small panels were sometimes set up to arbitrate in disputes or for conciliation purposes. Good reasons for not working a claim, such as illness, were recognized. Anyone who discovered a new placer deposit was rewarded by a double claim but nobody could acquire and hold more than two claims.

The essence of the system was that those involved in mining were the ones who ran it. There could be no absentee landlords, no buying up or consolidation of claims, and disputes were settled quickly and directly on the spot. This system of ordering and controlling claims was later extended, with small modifications, to cover tunnelling, water rights and quartz mining, as well as protecting the dirt-heaps built up by miners during the dry season,

which would be washed when water was available. The system worked and it was so successful that it was adopted, with little change, in other areas where new gold and silver deposits were worked: Oregon, Idaho, Arizona, New Mexico, Nevada and Montana.

This is not to say that the situation in the goldfields was ideal: men caught stealing were sometimes lynched on the spot. In 1855, for example, there were 47 illegal executions and 9 legal ones in California; 32 men were murdered in one year in Calaveras County alone.

This early kitchen at the AGC site had what may have been West Africa's first bread oven, foreground, right, to serve European dietary needs.

THE AUSTRALIAN STORY

A miner's life in the Australian goldfields in the early 1850s was also extremely hard, although state governments were able to exercise a higher degree of control and prevent the sort of violence and lynchings that had occurred in California. Special goldfield commissioners were appointed, licences had to be obtained and hard liquor was banned.

The large number of deaths among those who flocked to the Australian goldfields received far less publicity than the huge nuggets some miners found. Many of these miners were ill-fitted to the tough conditions of the diggings and succumbed. One writer observed, "The little levels between the stream and the mountain walls, for ten miles along the valley, are so thickly studded with graves that the river appears to run through a churchyard."

THE LARGE CORPORATIONS

In the closing decades of the 19th century and the early years of the 20th century, gold mining took on a new character. Once the most accessible and easily worked sources of gold had been exhausted, prospectors had no option but to leave, and the large mining corporations, with the power to gather the huge capital investment needed for deep mining and industrial extraction, took over.

Most of the goldfields discovered at the turn of the 20th century were, in any case, not workable by either a single miner or by small bands of miners. The Yukon field, after its first blaze of wealth, could only be profitably worked by dredging, a technique requiring large investment but few operators. Equally, the great Rand gold reefs of South Africa had complex geological structures that demanded new methods of extraction. The investment needed for this sort of mining and extraction was, and still is, enormous: in the 1880s half a million pounds was required to establish a mine. The operation of the new mines clearly depended on a labour force that offered its services in return for regular wages.

Thus the individual prospector with a bag of supplies, spade and gold pan was finally replaced by investment analysts, geologists, explosive specialists, chemists, safety experts and a myriad of other experts. In these changed circumstances, a new set of training and support services had to be developed to ensure the efficient working of miners as well as their safety.

Ashanti Miners – Then and Now

"From the 19th century onwards, mining ceased to be a one-sided profit industry, and workers started to enjoy the benefit of success."

We do not know exactly when people first began to extract gold in the forest zone in the Akan states, however, we do know that although the Ashanti came to dominate this area in the 18th and 19th centuries, gold was being won long before then. In all likelihood, the metal was being panned or dug out of placer deposits well before the 14th century. Although there is written evidence indicating that mine shafts were being dug by about 1700, mining by this method may go back far earlier.

We know that Akan gold was important to the world economy at this early date, we even know a good deal about their trading methods and the subsequent struggle with the Portuguese for control of the gold trade, but we know very little about the people who produced the gold itself. We do not know who the miners were, what their role and status in society were or how they were organized. Written accounts by Europeans describe "slaves" being employed in mining, while other accounts imply miners worked for themselves or on behalf of chiefs or kings. Nevertheless, the relationship between miner and superior is not clear.

In the 19th century some mining seems to have been carried out by groups of men and women who were obliged to work on particular days for their chiefs. Domestic slaves may also have been allocated to mining duties by their owners. We also know that

A key to AGC's progress has been the interaction between expatriates and their Ghanaian counterparts.

a tribal group called the *Nzema* from the southwest edge of the Western Region, had begun to be more or less professional miners, giving up farming and moving into other areas to develop new gold mines.

Even if some of the Ashanti gold mines were worked by "slaves" – and the evidence is still inconclusive – it is probable that the miners were generally treated with a degree of humanity that was unknown to the slaves of the Classical world and a far cry from the cruel and inhumane system established by the European powers in South America; in West Africa, unfree people still had legal rights. The Ashanti certainly obtained many domestic slaves by capture or tribute from surrounding groups, but they then absorbed many of these people into their society. Indeed, an outside observer would have found it difficult to distinguish "slaves" from ordinary "free" Ashantis as they went about their everyday activities.

One of the most basic rules of Ashanti life was that a person's origins were never to be mentioned, which was part and parcel of an underlying respect for individuals and for their role in the social structure. For this reason, even the lowest were treated with dignity and a degree of tolerance. It has been suggested that this rule enabled Ashanti, as it expanded, to absorb outsiders. Slave descendants were also absorbed into Ashanti society so that within a generation or two, the initial servitude could all but vanish.

When Europeans started mining in West Africa, the Ashantis were not enslaved as others had been before; and from the 19th century onwards, in Ashanti as in the rest of the world, mining ceased to be a one-sided profit industry and eventually workers, too, started to enjoy the benefits of success.

A steam boiler is erected in a forest clearing, and mining at Obuasi enters the industrial age. The early equipment was carried to the site from the coast as headloads of components.

THE ASHANTI GOLDFIELDS COMPANY
TODAY

Like many modern companies, AGC realizes that a healthy, well-trained workforce with high morale is a prerequisite for success, and to this end has set up a number of worker-related programmes, especially in the areas of training and inter-staff communication. Safety is a top priority and constant safety training has achieved significant reductions in numbers of work-related injuries. The company seeks continually to improve the technical skills of its workers and encourages a high degree of professionalism among the staff. The mining training school offers a wide range of courses, which means that several hundred employees each year are enabled to extend and strengthen their skill base in a number of different areas. When appropriate, opportunities are provided for staff to gain experience in mining operations outside Ghana so that their range of experience is broadened.

The end of a good day's work – a team of AGC miners with Prof. Edward Ayensu (centre) at an underground work site.

The group of statues, left, represents a miner and his family and is situated in the children's playground at the Bruno Estate, one of AGC's staff housing developments.

AGC also sponsors as many as 300 individuals each year who wish to pursue further education: this ranges from taking overseas Master's degrees and following correspondence courses to attending courses at local institutions, as well as seminars, conferences and other attachments. As one of Ghana's leading industrial companies, AGC attracts the best-qualified staff and employees. The terms of employment and payment for junior staff are agreed with the Ghana Mine Workers' Union.

Employees at all levels are encouraged to participate actively in the conduct of the company,

and every effort is made to promote and maintain stable, trouble-free working relations. Instrumental in this is a unique stratagem known as "Free Speak". This allows employees, selected at random and from all ranks in the hierarchy, not only to air their grievances but also to put forward any constructive suggestions they may have about the running of the company.

Mining and the local community

Away from the workplace, AGC attaches enormous importance to projects which benefit not only its own employees, but also the local community. The provision of health care, educational and leisure facilities for employees and their dependants are priority concerns, and a number of successful projects are either in place or in the course of development. These include the construction of new housing, which has opened up the Obuasi township and led to increased local economic activities. This has formed the basis for new employment opportunities for young people, who hitherto could only become miners.

AGC's 150-bed hospital along with its Obuasi Health Centre are open to the whole Obuasi township as well as to surrounding villages. Regular health checks and clinics are available for everyone involved in mining and the support services. Under

The Junior Secondary School, top right, was built by AGC to serve its staff's families. The company dominates the town of Obuasi, and among the school's 400 students are children of residents associated with the mine. Another 1,000 youngsters attend the primary school, centre right. A former school building, below right, now houses the company museum, displaying some of the mine's original equipment.

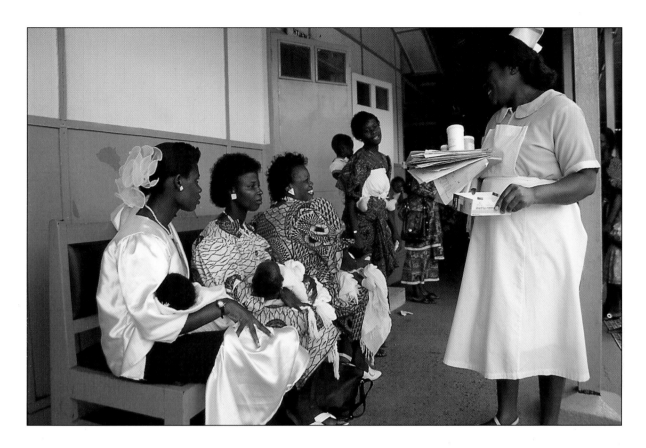

At the Ashanti Goldfields Company's own hospital, mothers are given the most up-to-date in pre- and post-natal care. The hospital is open to both AGC staff in Obuasi and the locals in Obuasi and its environs.

the community assistance programme, the company is also providing a public library in Obuasi. In 1992, the company extended its already wide range of sporting and leisure facilities with the opening of the Len Clay Stadium. In addition to providing a home for the nation's Football League champions – the Goldfields Football Club – the stadium also provides a first-class sporting venue for the local community.

Recognizing that its mining activities have a profound impact on people living on and around the mining concession areas, which may lead to a disruption or breakdown of cultural and traditional values, the company strives to minimize or mitigate any negative effects on the environment and on the

lives and livelihoods of local people. Keen to establish good working relationships with members of the local community, AGC encourages discussion of matters of concern either through the District Assembly, of which it is a member, or directly with local leaders.

The company has always respected the rights of the local authority, and the traditional political and social institutions have all benefited from this relationship. Before entering or applying for a mining concession, AGC must meet all the legal requirements set out by the Ministry and Forestry Commissions as well as by other relevant authorities. Meetings at which the company's intentions are explained are arranged with traditional leaders. Compensation for land, and royalties from the mining, are assessed by government and paid by mining companies to chiefs and individuals.

The company also supplements government

The Goldfields football team, above, sponsored by AGC, has won the national division one league championship on several occasions. The team's managers run a soccer academy which grooms talented players from all over the country.

The AGC band, The Gold Nuggets, top left, shows that mining is not all about work. The Nuggets play traditional and popular music and perform at various AGC and other functions.

The Atenteben, *traditional flute players, left, are part of a cultural display by the students of the AGC School.*

efforts in the provision of social services and road-building by assisting local communities with a number of infrastructural projects. Water is a vital requirement in and around concession areas and since 1990–91 the company has supplied 70 boreholes with handpumps for populations of 500 or more, and hand-dug wells for a further 67 villages with smaller populations. Within the Obuasi township itself, AGC has provided 15 boreholes with handpumps and two spring boxes. All work conforms to government guidelines, and water quality is monitored according to the World Health Organization standards.

There is also a major project to bring electricity to villages – the villages of Sansu and Odumase already draw free electricity from AGC and five villages in the Amansie West District will get electricity once the necessary infrastructure is in place. Other services to the community provided by AGC include the provision of fully furnished classroom blocks for the villages of Odumase and Jimisokakraba as well as the desilting of the Kwabrafo stream in Obuasi.

AGC constantly strives to manage its community relations better. While continuing to support the villages in and around its mining concessions the company also encourages traditional rulers who receive royalties to do more for their communities.

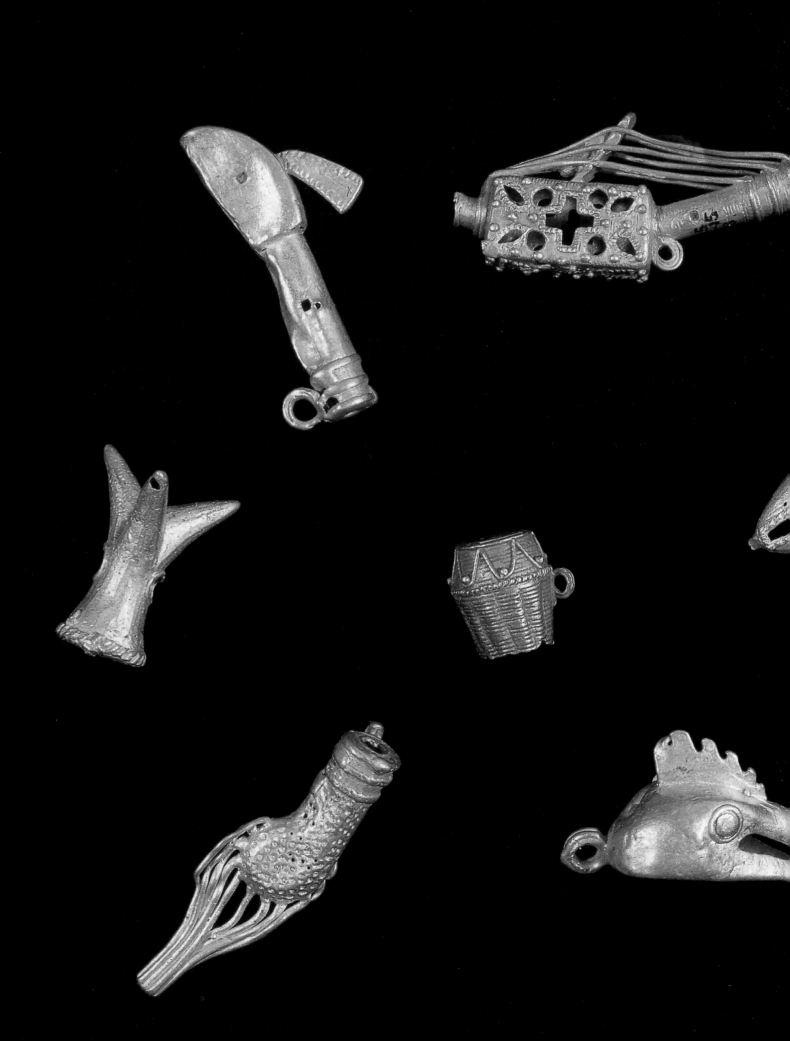

THE SPREAD OF GOLD

For all its value, gold remains anonymous, its source unidentifiable. But once it is in circulation its impact is decisive. The gold covering a bejewelled Indian bride could have been extracted from the hills of Obuasi but bought from the stalls in a Dubai gold market where gold chains are sold by length.

THE SPREAD OF GOLD

"Once extracted from the earth it can be made into artefacts or coins, melted down again, turned into bars or jewellery, sold, smuggled, looted or stolen; changing its appearance but retaining its essential character."

Gold mined in the Ashanti forests 300 years ago, carried to the coast, shipped to London, turned into English guineas and passed from hand to hand for decades, then melted down again, may today form part of an Indian bride's dowry. Because of its remarkable anonymity we cannot always tell where any particular piece of gold began its journey, although we can get a broad idea of how gold has spread around the world since it first began to be valued. Throughout history, gold has been moved across the world, its presence indicating power, its absence decline and defeat; and gold, in this context, cannot usually be divorced from its use as money. Although some groups, such as the Ashanti, continued to use gold dust as a currency until this century, most of its monetary use has been in the form of coins.

The invention of coins, quantities of metal of fixed mass and of agreed value, is attributed to the Lydians, Greek inhabitants of what is now western Turkey, some time late in the 7th century BC. Creating coins was a revolutionary step, making all sorts of exchanges easier and quicker. Virtually everything that could be counted, measured or weighed could also be given a value measured in coins. This enabled sellers to hold on to the value of

This gold pectoral decoration has three large sunflower-like patterns as the central motifs. Pieces of this shape are said to have been worn by the priests of Ashanti gods.

what they sold until the time was ripe for them to take other items in exchange for it. Once coins had been "invented", much of the world's gold and silver was destined to be used in this form.

The earliest coins were made of electrum, a natural alloy of gold and silver, but the first pure gold and silver coins are traditionally ascribed to Croesus of Lydia (561–546 BC), a ruler who is also said to have sent 3,400 kg (7,500 lb) of gold to decorate the temple at Delphi, Greece. Gold coins, however, were comparatively rare in the Classical world; they were normally outnumbered by silver, which was more readily available, or by bronze. The Athenians, for example, only minted gold coins in an emergency, stripping the gold from statues to do so. As Greek power expanded, more gold was coined. In the 4th century BC, Philip of Macedon obtained enough gold for the regular minting of gold coins; and his son, Alexander the Great, was able to greatly extend the area in which gold coins circulated, having seized the hoarded gold treasures of the pharaohs and the Achaemenids of the Persian Empire and gained control of gold sources farther east.

Gold coins were rarely struck under the Roman Republic but Imperial Rome began to use them. The gold *solidus* struck by the emperor Constantine remained unchanged in its weight and purity until the Empire itself disappeared. Many of the gold coins made under the Empire, however, seem to have been traded out of it into India and the Far East.

TRAVELLING EAST

After the fall of the western Roman Empire gold coins tended to disappear from circulation, for the most part being replaced by silver coins debased to varying degrees. One problem was that the West was short of gold. The contrast with the Islamic world was striking. In the 690s the Caliphate started minting a gold coin that was soon to be accepted from Spain to Malaya. This was the dinar, its name derived from *denarius aureus*, the gold *solidus* coin of the late Roman Empire. The dinar set the standard for purity and wide acceptability for centuries to come: it penetrated into Christian Europe, sometimes continuing to be used in trade, sometimes turned into jewellery and ornaments. The abundance of gold in Islamic countries had a great deal to do with their access to the gold-producing areas of West Africa. The great network of overland trade routes from those areas existed largely to pump gold into the Islamic countries where dynasties like the Almoravids of Morocco minted it into dinars.

West African gold sometimes came into circulation outside Africa in more direct way. When the great King of Mali, Mansa Musa, who ruled between 1307 and 1332, made the pilgrimage to Mecca, he took 500 slaves with him and so much gold, that after he left prices in Cairo took three years to get back to their old levels.

Gold coins clearly carried a high level of prestige. A country minting gold indicated both wealth and stability, allowing it to command easier trade terms simply because people trusted the purity and constant weight of its coinage. Thus the revival of the European economy in the 13th century was signalled by the reappearance of gold coins. The emperor Frederick II, for reasons of prestige, issued gold coins in 1231. In 1252, Florence issued the *fiorino d'oro*, or florin, and Genoa the *genovino d'oro*. Venice issued the ducat in 1284, France had gold coins by 1330, and the English noble dates from 1351. Some of this gold

must have been obtained from Islamic countries by trade, possibly in exchange for silver, a metal Europe had far more of, and some probably came from new gold mines in Hungary.

THE "SILENT TRADE"

The movement of Europeans around the world from the 15th century on, aided by their increasingly efficient sailing vessels with unprecedented firepower, caused major changes in the movement of gold and an increase in its circulation as coins. The Portuguese, for example, captured the North African coastal town of Ceuta in 1415 and learned from the

Glittering and exquisitely crafted gold is used on an extraordinary scale to decorate the upper storey interior of the Golden Temple at Amritsar.

Moors of gold-rich lands on the Upper Niger and in Senegal. This was the era of what has been described as "silent trade", when the Moors, trading with the Akans who occupied present-day Ghana, obtained large quantities of gold (as well as slaves, ivory and pepper) in exchange for iron, pewter basins, brass, pots, pans, knives, daggers and salt. Until the 19th century, salt was a particularly important item for barter in West Africa. Indeed, one gold-producing forest tribe was so much in need of it, they were willing to exchange salt for gold, weight for weight.

THE GOLD COAST TRADE

It was not until 1471, however, that the Portuguese finally reached the Gold Coast, under the command of Juan de Santarem and Pedro de Escobar. They landed at Shama near the estuary of the Pra River

This brass vessel, or kuduo, *is decorated with designs that are of Islamic origin. This is a direct result of trading over the Sahara.*

and here the European trade in gold began. Diego d'Azambuja, who followed the route of Santarem, sailed to the Gold Coast to trade in gold with the people who lived in an area that the Portuguese would come to call El Mine (the Mine), hence Elmina, and where in 1482 they would built a fort.

On one trip, d'Azambuja had on board a sailor engaged in cartographic work: some believe that it was Christopher Columbus. On completion of this project he was to be commissioned by the queen of Spain to discover a westward route to the Indies to find gold – a route that led eventually to his accidental landing on the American mainland.

The Dutch, who had arrived at the Gold Coast in 1595, captured Elmina in 1637 and had taken over all Portuguese possessions by 1642. At this time, British traders were also active. Despite Dutch efforts to expel them, the British maintained their footing and, after hostilities in 1664–65, the two parties concluded a peace treaty in 1667. By 1750, there were only the Danes at Christianborg Castle, the Dutch at Elmina and the British at Cape Coast Castle still trading. In 1850 the Danes left, the Dutch in 1872, leaving the British in complete control of a thriving trade in gold dust and nuggets.

THE EFFECTS OF TRADE

Not only does the movement of gold from one area of the globe to another set great changes in motion in the recipient states, but it also has a profound effect on the producing society.

The gold that flowed out of the Akan forests caused major changes in the society of the Ashanti and the surrounding peoples. The gold trade effectively tied them into the rest of the world and they soon became inextricably linked to the developing capitalist and industrial system of Europe, a system which, by the 19th century, came to dominate the whole globe.

EXPANDING HORIZONS

The gold trade to the north of the Ashantis, over the Sahelian belt, had already introduced new goods and new ideas, perhaps even new mining techniques, by the time the Portuguese arrived on the scene. The *Wangara* traders who came from the north to obtain gold provided valuable commodities in exchange: salt, North African cloth and metal items. Among the most valued of the latter were bowls and other brass vessels made in Egypt or North Africa, decorated with elaborate designs and texts in Arabic script. Vessels of this sort were highly valued by the Akans and they entered into their early traditions and mythologies: the founding ancestors of some groups are said to have come down from the sky in brass basins and such vessels were used as shrines for their gods or treated as sacred relics. Later, the Ashanti and other groups began making their own copies of them, creating the type of ritual vessel known as the *kuduo*, which were decorated in patterns copied from the original Islamic imports. The knowledge of Islamic design and script introduced in this way may also have influenced the patterns used in Ashanti art. The incoming traders also used a system of weights for measuring out gold which influenced the development of local weights.

The local need to find gold in order to trade for exotic goods set in train vast changes that eventually led to the creation of a system of an elaborate centralized government in Ashanti. When the first traders arrived, the ancestors of the Ashanti were probably living in small communities scattered through the rain forest, subsisting by a combination of hunting and horticulture. The gold trade gave them another source of livelihood and, apart from importing necessary items such as salt and cloth, it also allowed them to import slaves in return for the gold they were producing.

Most Europeans arrived at the Gold Coast in the hope of finding wealth, but many simply found malaria and other tropical diseases and ended up here, in the European Cemetery, Elmina.

Portuguese traders or officials are depicted in the plaques above and below. The Elmina Castle, pictured opposite, was the centre of Portuguese trading activities and was the departure point for slaves as well as gold.

GOLD AND THE SLAVE TRADE

When the Portuguese began to fight their way into the gold trade they discovered that there was a great demand for human labour in the interior, that is, in the areas where the gold was being produced. In order to profit from this demand they began to buy or capture slaves in the area of Benin and ship them to the Gold Coast. There, once they were exchanged for gold, they were taken inland.

Why was there this demand? What were all these extra hands needed for? Although the process is unclear, it seems that the Akan were undergoing a sort of agricultural revolution. Areas of the dense rain forest were being cleared to allow more productive farming. As productivity rose, so the forest was able to support a larger population, grouped together in bigger settlements. The labour they bought in exchange for gold supported this process.

TRADING WITH THE WORLD

By the 16th century, Akan society had reached a take-off point and exported gold provided much of the power that enabled it to do so. But the gold trade did not end once local society had begun to move into a period of population growth and increasing prosperity. Gold, traded to Europeans, could provide other resources which served to increase the power of those who controlled local gold production. These included: slaves, cloth, iron, beads, brass, distilled liquor and, most importantly, firearms. The Ashanti used their guns to expand the resources under their control. For much of the 18th and early 19th centuries theirs was a growing economy, fuelled by war, conquest, booty and levies as well as by trade.

While trade links with the wider world helped Ashanti society to evolve, they also had the power to damage it. When the slave trade was abolished in the 1820s the Asantehene found himself in considerable difficulty because the slave trade had developed into an important part of the Ashanti economy. Equally, when trade was depressed in Europe or the Americas the Ashanti suffered. But the Ashanti developed a great understanding of trade, establishing systems of credit and always being ready to embark on new enterprises if they felt they could show a profit. Besides gold, they exported caffeine-rich kola nuts (mostly to the north where their power to suppress appetite and tiredness was especially valued by Muslims, denied the use of tobacco on religious grounds) and, later, rubber and cocoa beans.

TREASURE BENEATH THE WAVES

The movement of large amounts of gold across the world by sea has never been without mishaps and disasters. This is especially the case when one group is trying to move gold and its rivals are trying to prevent them doing so. The great Spanish treasure fleets that carried gold and silver back from the New World were seen as legitimate prey by Spain's European rivals, who were also happy to seize the bullion that piled up in Panama or Cartagena awaiting transportation to Spain.

Other disasters also prevented the movement of South American gold around the world: the most usual of these was shipwreck, and great quantities of gold were lost at sea in this way. Not only were the fleets constantly at risk from attack by the ships of other nations, but the season for safe sailing was brief. The various vessels of the Spanish treasure fleets would assemble in Cuba towards the end of summer ready to set out for Europe. But from June to October there were severe hurricanes along the South Atlantic route and, if departure was delayed to avoid these, the fleet then stood a very good chance of running into bad weather in the north Atlantic.

If a treasure ship went down and its position was known, the Spanish authorities usually made strenuous attempts to salvage its cargo. This occurred after the sinking of the *Nostra Señora de Atocha* and the *Santa Margarita* off the Florida Keys in 1622. The *Atocha* could be located by one of its masts protruding out of the water. It lay at about 17 m (55 ft)

The women of Ghana would have treasured jewellery such as this locally made gold bracelet and necklace. However, gold jewellery was often taken abroad by ship only to be lost at sea.

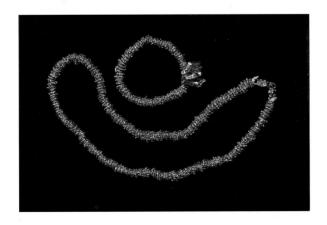

and pearl divers were sent down to attempt to salvage its cargo of gold, silver and emeralds. But it was just at the limit of their diving capacity and they could stay down only for a few moments. Before much could be achieved the wreck vanished, buried under shifting sands. The *Santa Margarita* was then located and about 67,000 silver coins and 380 gold ingots were recorded as having been recovered before the salvage operation ended.

There things rested until a few decades ago, the stories of the *Santa Margarita* and *Atocha* having become part of that fascinating mixture of truth and legend that grows up around lost treasure ships. Then, a group of professional treasure hunters began to look for the wrecks, finally locating the *Santa Margarita*. Fascinatingly, a West African connection keeps intruding into this story. In 1973, a young American archaeologist called Duncan Mathewson, who had worked in Ghana, was hired to strengthen the team's expertise; later he recruited Professor Jim Bellis, another American who had excavated in Ghana and done work on early Akan gold mining. Not only this: among the silver bars eventually recovered was one intended to pay tax on the sale of West African slaves at Cartagena. It took until 1985 for the *Atocha* to be found.

"PRIAM'S TREASURE"

Gold does not have to be sunk to be termed "lost treasure". A particularly interesting story, shrouded in mystery and secrecy, is that of one of the most famous collections of gold artefacts from antiquity, the gold of Troy, discovered in the early 1870s by Heinrich Schliemann. A highly successful German businessman turned archaeologist, Schliemann's passion in life was to find the legendary city of Troy, described by Homer in the *Iliad* and the *Odyssey*. He was convinced by the arguments of Frank Calvert, an expert on Trojan antiquities, that the ruins of Troy lay under a hill (part of which Calvert owned) at

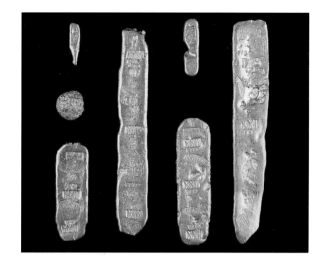

Gold bars were retrieved *from the wreck of the* Nuestra Señora De Las Marvillas, *which sank on the way to Spain. Her cargo included a 1.5-m (5-ft) solid-gold Madonna from Panama.*

Hissarlik in Turkey. Here Schliemann started digging (without official permission) and eventually discovered 8,830 objects made of gold, electrum, silver and bronze, which he named Priam's treasure, after the last king of Troy.

The treasure was, in the first instance, secretly smuggled into Athens, but a scandal broke out and Schliemann was taken to court by the Turkish government and he had to buy the treasure from them and pay a fine. Because of the secrecy surrounding the excavations and the ambiguity in recording the circumstances in which the treasure was found, there was a lot of controversy surrounding its authenticity and no museum wanted to accept it. Museums such as the Louvre in Paris and the Hermitage in St Petersburg refused to accept the gold of Troy. Schliemann moved it to Berlin where it was thought to have disappeared during the Second World War. Years later, it was discovered that in the last days of the war, when the gold of Troy was in danger of being destroyed, the director of the Museum of Ancient History in Berlin secretly handed the treasure over to the Soviet Military, and it was

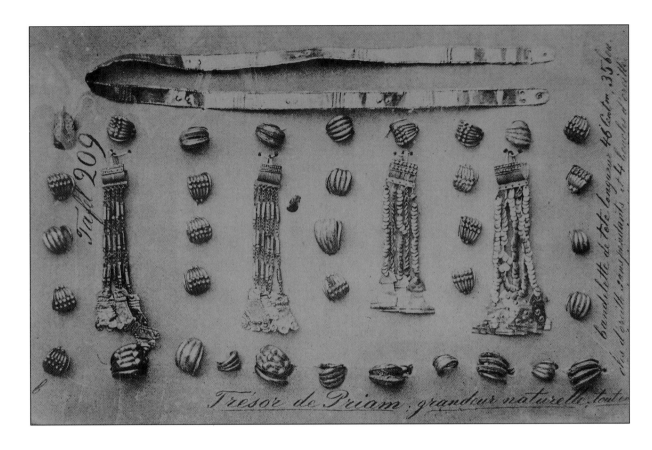

Trésor de Priam grandeur naturelle toute

taken to Russia for safe-keeping. Almost 50 years later, after disappearing and re-appearing all over Europe, the gold of Troy was finally displayed in the Pushkin State Museum of Fine Arts in Moscow.

Heinrich Schliemann discovered 8,830 objects made of gold, electrum, silver and bronze, which he named Priam's treasure, after the last king of Troy. Schliemann's wife is pictured below wearing some of the treasure.

SMUGGLING GOLD

The anonymity of gold, and the fact that a very small amount has a very considerable value, has made it an ideal material for both the amateur and the professional smuggler. When demand is high in one area and there are government controls on buying or owning gold, the smuggler steps in. A decent margin between the selling price of gold in one place and the buying price in another sets this unofficial movement going.

The history of the world in the last 200 years has involved the creation of numerous new states whose boundaries take little or no account of traditional allegiances, ethnic groupings or even natural geographical divisions. The colonial division of Africa, with its many ruler-straight boundaries cutting through single ethnic and linguistic groups, has produced divisions that are still not accepted by the people forced to live in these different countries. In these instances, "smuggling" may be nothing more than the continuation of traditional trading patterns in which some locals feel governments have no right to interfere.

Land and sea borders make for easier gold smuggling than routes that involve air travel. These days airlines' fear of terrorism ensures that most

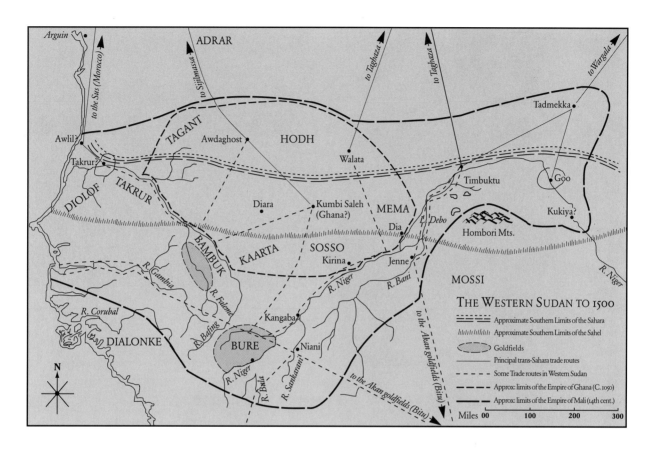

THE WESTERN SUDAN TO 1500

	Approximate Southern Limits of the Sahara
	Approximate Southern Limits of the Sahel
	Goldfields
	Principal trans-Sahara trade routes
	Some Trade routes in Western Sudan
	Approx: limits of the Empire of Ghana (C. 1050)
	Approx: limits of the Empire of Mali (14th cent.)

Miles 00   100   200   300

passengers have to pass through metal detectors at airports and their hand luggage be X-rayed, but when the crucial border is on land, smuggling becomes much easier for both professional and non-professional operators. The simplest form of smuggling is also the hardest to prevent: non-professionals concealing small quantities of the metal about – or even inside – their bodies and carrying it over a border.

Sometimes there is no real attempt at concealing smuggled gold: many Ashanti and other Ghanaian women, for example, traditionally wear strings of fine beads around their waists and nowadays some of these are made of gold. It would take a very brave customs officer to suggest that they were not purely for personal adornment. Interestingly enough, these golden waist beads may have smuggling parallels in the 16th and 17th centuries: gold chains, some as long as 4 m (12 ft), have been recovered from sunken

This map shows the old trade routes from the Sahelian belt into the Ashanti Empire. Today, similar routes may well be used to smuggle gold over land into the Middle East.

Spanish treasure galleons and it has been suggested that these were a way of smuggling gold in the guise of personal jewellery.

Today, stories abound of illegally excavated gold dust and nuggets being smuggled out of Ghana and into neighbouring and faraway places in recent years. It may be hidden away in balls of kenkey, a local food made of fermented and steamed maize, or in yams with the incisions plastered over and hidden with mud. Other methods are even simpler: the smuggler simply crosses the border at a point where there are no roads or paths and no border guards and customs officials. Some ingenious hiding places are found in obscure parts of the lorries and buses that regularly leave Ghana for the surrounding countries. Gold can

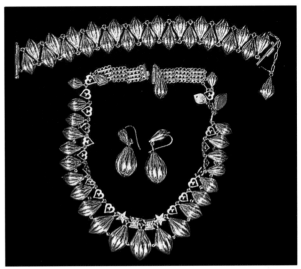

The jewellery above, depicting cocoa pods, was made in Ghana but similar pieces, like other gold ornaments, can be found in gold markets all over the Middle and Far East.

The golden altar in the church on the left was covered in tar to hide it from thieves and rogues in Panama.

In Dubai, India and Sri Lanka there are markets and duty-free shops like the one on the right where gold can be freely bought.

be concealed inside the sump, in a false compartment within the fuel tank, or attached inside one of the wheels before the tyre is fitted. Checking every inch of these vehicles is impossible and the only chance of a smuggler being detected is by luck or betrayal.

THE SPREAD OF GOLD TODAY

People all over the world want gold. When they fear that the world economy is collapsing, that their government may fall and its paper currency prove worthless, or that they may have to flee for their lives, their need for it increases. In times of war, gold may be the most acceptable currency of all: during the Second World War, for example, British agents operating in the Balkans had to pay for support and goods in gold sovereigns. Where there are price differences in gold, where governments forbid their citizens to hold it,

where there is fear for the future, smugglers step in to meet the demand and make a profit.

The desire for gold is particularly evident in India today. Gold is the traditional gift to brides and a handy way for them to keep their fortune in the form of jewellery until it is needed. Families and individuals hoard considerable quantities of the metal, partly as an insurance against bad times, partly to conceal money from the taxman, partly to safeguard against falls in the value of paper currency. The Indian Reserve Bank estimated in 1958 that there were no less than 3,150 tonnes of gold in private hands in India. A great deal of gold is smuggled into the well-known gold markets of the subcontinent by fast diesel-powered dhows. A staging post is often a jewellery-making centre, such as Dubai.

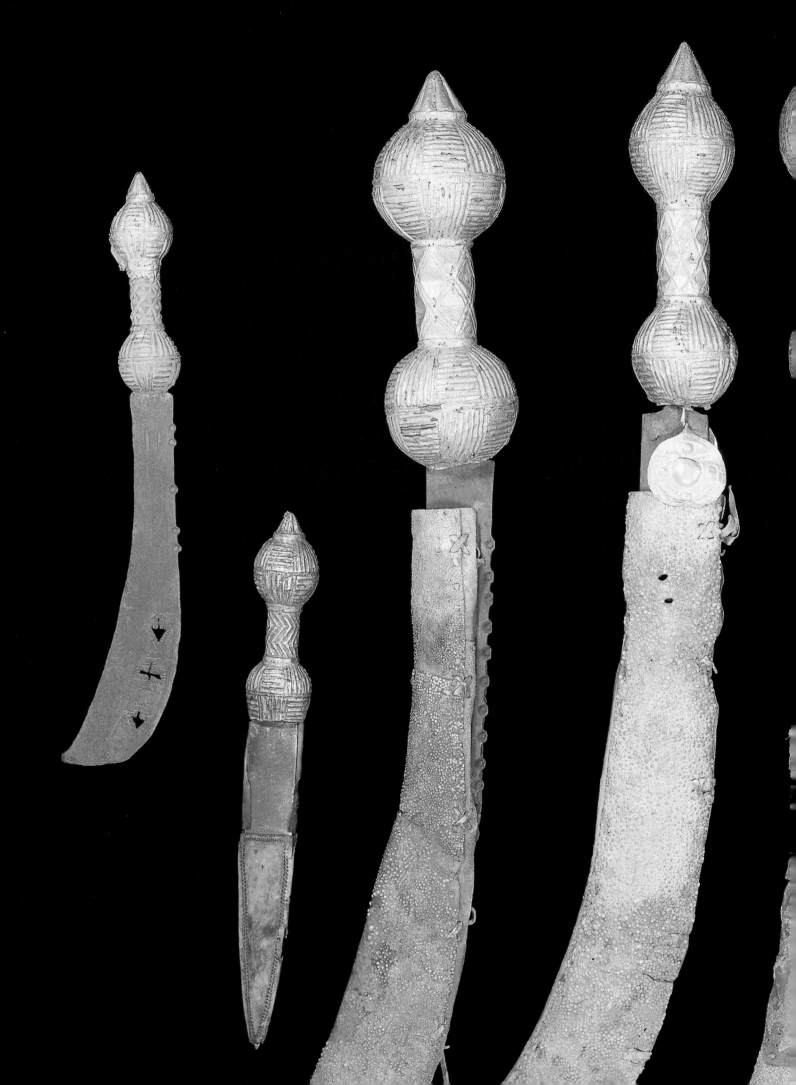

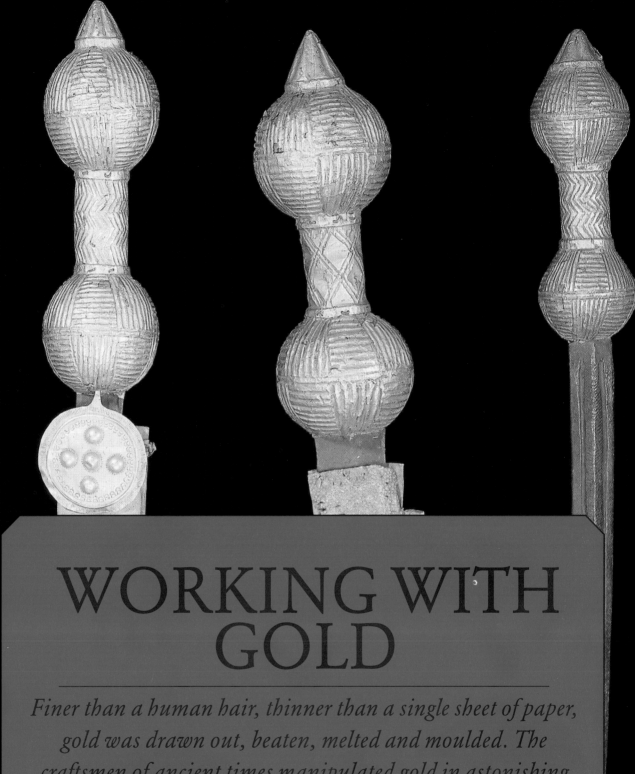

WORKING WITH
GOLD

Finer than a human hair, thinner than a single sheet of paper, gold was drawn out, beaten, melted and moulded. The craftsmen of ancient times manipulated gold in astonishing ways to glorify the world, from adorning the greatest temples to the casting of delicate jewellery.

WORKING WITH GOLD

"Most of the ways in which gold is worked today were invented thousands of years ago by unknown craftsmen, using the simplest of tools."

Throughout recorded history gold has been used to glorify kings and queens and to adorn the temples of gods. It has been shaped to make the most elaborate and elegant of artefacts and to adorn the most important works of architecture. The metal itself has such power and attraction that cunning ways have been found to cover objects made from far less valuable materials, such as wood or base metal, with a bright casing of gold.

Paintings on the walls of Egyptian tombs show goldsmiths at work and it is clear that their equipment was basic: bellows to heat their small furnaces, stone hammers to flatten the metal and simple hand tools to cut and shape it. Their real expertise in working gold lay in their extensive knowledge of its physical properties and their experience, keen eyes and manual skill.

The knowledge and skill of ancient goldsmiths is astonishing. Many of the gold items made today pay silent tribute to the inventiveness and skill of craftsmen four or five thousand years ago. Pieces recovered from the royal graves at Ur, dated to about 2,600 BC, reveal an extensive metallurgical knowledge. Early goldsmiths were fully aware of the ductility and malleability of gold and its resistance to tarnishing and they took advantage of these qualities. They also understood how the metal could be alloyed and how to control accurately the

Ashanti rings and pendants are formed in all kinds of shapes and designs. Most of the animals and other decorations usually have a symbolic meaning.

temperature to which they heated it. Artefacts show that they were familiar with the techniques of raising and repoussé. Raising is the process of beating – and so gradually extending – an initial slab of gold against a shaped block, and is a process practised by the more skilled goldsmiths today. A basic shape raised in this way could then be decorated by hammering it from the inside to produce raised areas on the outside, in what is now called repoussé work, another technique still in common use. After that the outer surface of the vessel would be given more decoration by scribing and punching it with hard metal tools, again a working method with which modern gold workers are familiar.

WIRE WORK

The earliest form of gold wire, from the time of the Sumerians, was produced by cutting long strips from a thin sheet of gold and then rounding them either by hammering or by rolling them between two hard surfaces, probably slabs of stone or wood.

Down the centuries, gold wire has been woven into textiles, wrapped around thread that was used to embroider garments, or coiled around a core of some lesser material to produce bracelets or rings. It has also been soldered to backing plates of gold to make elaborately decorated jewellery or joined together to make openwork earrings or pendants – filigree work – often producing objects of the utmost complexity and delicacy. At the earliest stages of the evolution of this craft the gold wire was anchored in place with tiny gold pins, thin strips of the metal or tied on with

other lengths of wire. Later, ways were found to solder it in place.

Today, one tonne of gold can be stretched into wire long enough to reach from the earth to the moon and back again. The modern method of making gold wire, and wire from other metals, uses a draw-plate. This is a slab of hard metal, now usually steel or iron but in the past probably bronze, through which holes of different diameters are drilled. To make wire, a piece of gold is cast or hammered into a roughly pointed cylindrical shape so that one end will just protrude through the largest hole in the draw-plate. The draw-plate is firmly anchored (a 15th-century engraving shows the operator standing on it) and the protruding length of gold is steadily pulled through the hole, stretching and thinning as it goes. After all the gold has been pulled through the largest hole the process is repeated through the next-largest hole, then the next, and so on, the gold getting thinner and longer with every drawing, until it is sufficiently fine. At each stage the wire is annealed to prevent it becoming brittle.

SOLDERING

Knowledge of how to join different pieces of gold together with solder dates from at least 5,500 years ago, when it was used in Mesopotamia. Until soldering was invented, separate pieces of metal could only be joined by riveting the individual pieces together with "stitches" or by bending their edges over and hammering them together.

This ancient Greek gold crown, dating from c. 400 BC, is decorated with hammered gold leaves as well as gold granules. Granulation is a technique that was developed and mastered by the Etruscans.

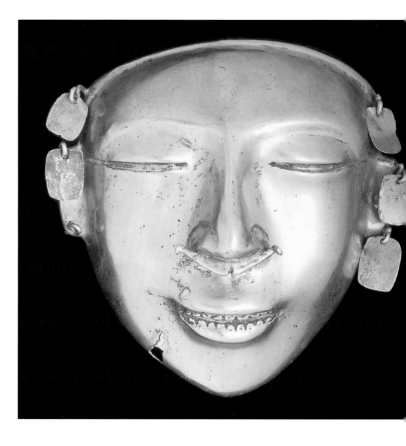

This gold mask from Quimbaya (Colombia) dates from 600 to 1100 AD; such masks were usually used to cover the faces of the dead.

The invention of soldering allowed the creation of complex pieces with far stronger joints. The key to this technique lies in producing an alloy that will bond with gold but will melt and make the join at a temperature well below the melting point of gold. This is to make sure that when the solder is heated and runs into place, there is no danger that the carefully shaped pieces of gold, which it is meant to join, will also melt and lose their form.

GRANULATION

The technique of granulation – decorating a plain gold surface with minute spheres of gold – was one of the most complex to be invented in antiquity. By the 7th century BC the Etruscans were masters of this technique and their work shows great technical skill

coupled with a wonderful sense of design. The first step in the process was to make the spherical granules, which were as small as one-quarter of a millimetre (one-hundreth of an inch) in diameter. This was done by melting very tiny clippings or filings of gold, or a small quantity of natural gold dust. When it was molten the surface tension of the liquid gold allowed it to form perfect spheres; they were not flattened by the force of gravity because of their small size.

This girl is one of two virgins, called Mprakyirie, *chosen from the royal household to be adorned with gold trinkets and given a whisk to ward off evil spirits that may follow the Asantehene.*

The tiny balls of gold were sorted into different sizes by sieving them. Next, they had to be soldered to the surface they were to decorate. Getting hundreds of spheres this small into position, let alone soldering them in place, may seem almost impossible. A way had to be found to hold each

sphere in its exact location and then the solder had to be put in precisely the correct place. What is more, the film of solder had to be so thin that it did not drown the spheres, and the temperature had to be high enough to melt the solder, but not high enough to melt the spheres.

The ingenious process that made all this possible was invented in the ancient world. The technique involved introducing copper between the gold spheres and the gold base to which they were to be attached, and then making the copper form an alloy with both lots of gold. In the first step, substances containing copper carbonate or copper oxide were ground to a fine powder and mixed with paint or glue. This mixture was painted on to the gold base in the places to be decorated with the granules. The granules were then carefully placed on the sticky surface which held them in place. The next stage was to heat the object to a temperature a little below the melting point of gold. In the presence of heat and a plentiful supply of air, the copper oxide or carbonate of copper was reduced. This means that copper in molten metallic form was released and this molten copper then formed an alloy with the gold of the granules and the gold of the surface beneath them, thus invisibly soldering them both together. If the heating continued, the copper could be made to diffuse, to become completely "soaked up" into both lots of gold, to all intents and purposes disappearing and leaving an invisible joint.

CASTING

In the course of history many gold items have been made by casting, that is, pouring molten metal into a mould to give the desired form once it has cooled and hardened. A lot of casting was done by the lost-wax process – a technique at which Ashanti goldsmiths excelled – but re-usable moulds, made of stone, were also utilized. The design is cut into the face of the stone, much like an impressed shape.

The metal is poured in and then extracted once it has cooled and shrunk slightly. Open moulds are used when only one surface, the one taking the impression, is important. For double-faced castings two moulds were fitted together and the metal poured down a channel into the space they contained.

HIGH-TECH GOLD CLAY

A recent Japanese invention could render traditional forms of casting obsolete. Gold clay, made of powdered gold (each speck less than 20 microns in diameter) blended with water and a special binder, looks and feels like ordinary potter's clay, and can be worked in much the same way. It can be shaped by hand, turned on a wheel and carved with modelling

When the court crier (Nseniekye) *is not wearing his cap made of animal skin covered with gold, he hangs it around his neck like a talisman.*

tools. It only has to be left for a couple of days to dry before being fired at around 1,000°C (1,832°F) in order to evaporate the water, burn off the binder and fuse the tiny grains of gold together. What then emerges is a solid gold object that is actually harder than gold cast or shaped by conventional methods. This allows the goldsmith to use a purer gold that might otherwise have been too soft to use in a particular situation.

Gold leaf

Over the centuries much human ingenuity has been expended on making a small amount of gold go a long way. One way to do this is to make it into thin sheet or even thinner leaf. Even when beaten into an almost invisible film, gold retains its resistance to

The Golden Rock is situated on the edge of a cliff in Burma. It is almost completely covered in gold leaf, which people have placed there piece by piece as a sign of devotion.

corrosion. Today, gold leaf 0.1 micron (one-ten-thousandth of a millimetre or four-millionths of an inch) thick can be manufactured. Beaten this thin, one ounce of gold would cover 23 sq m (250 sq ft). For most practical purposes, however, a heavier gauge of gold leaf is manufactured.

The practice of using gold leaf to decorate important and sacred objects was widespread in the ancient world. The Israelites used it to cover the Tabernacle, and Homer mentions Bronze Age Greeks gilding the horns of sacrificial oxen. The Romans used large quantities of the material to decorate important buildings throughout their empire. More recently, when the 80-m (260-ft) high spire of St Petersburg's Admiralty Building was being restored by the old Soviet regime, 2 kg (4½ lb) of gold leaf were used to cover it. The fineness of gold leaf has another advantage besides its incorruptibility; it will normally mould itself around whatever object it is used to cover, allowing all but the most complex of shapes to be gilded and protected.

Egyptian gold workers 5,000 years ago may have been the first to manufacture very thin sheets of gold, although it is possible that they learned the technique from earlier craftsmen. The basic procedure has hardly changed since, and the samples of gold leaf recovered from Tutankhamen's tomb differ little from those produced today. A 12th-century account of gold-leaf manufacture cites the only major innovation introduced since that period: the interleaving of the metal with materials such as parchment during the beating process. In its essentials this method is still used to make gold leaf.

Beating and quartering

Nowadays, an initial thin sheet of gold is produced by a machine which rolls the metal out in a ribbon 25 microns thick (one-fortieth of a millimetre or one-thousandth of an inch). Gold used for making leaf has a high degree of purity, 23 karats or more,

with small amounts of copper or silver added to alter the colour of the gold as required. Any further alloying would make the resulting metal too brittle to be thinned in this way. Small squares of gold are cut from this ribbon and 200–400 of them are layered between sheets of special paper or parchment, which softens the blows from the hammer. The layers are wrapped tightly in strong paper to keep the stack in alignment. After it has been beaten for about half an hour, each square of gold will have thinned and increased in size to about a 10-cm (4-in) square.

Each square is then carefully taken out and cut into quarters. Each quarter piece is next sandwiched between sheets of special paper and beaten again till it extends to the edge of the paper. The 10-cm (4-in) squares are once more cut into quarters and this time interleaved with "gold beaters' skins" made from bovine intestines. As the leaf becomes thinner it

Thousands of tiny squares of gold leaf adhere to many statues in Buddhist temples in Thailand. These signs of devotion are purchased by worshippers on their way in to the temple.

becomes increasingly difficult to handle. It will stick to metal tools so it has to be picked up and manipulated with boxwood pincers and cut with blades made from sharp slivers of rattan cane.

This process of beating and quartering and beating again means that at the final stage 64 squares of leaf have been produced from each of the original squares. At the final stage, once the desired thickness has been reached, the leaves are placed in books of rouged tissues, each of which holds 25 sheets of gold. If the leaf is to be used for gilding in situations where it may easily be blown away, sheets of non-rouged tissue, to which the leaf will cling, are inserted into the pages of the book. Once the leaf has adhered to these sheets the gilder can handle it confidently via

Chiefs sit in state, with their linguists displaying their staffs of office. The various figures on the staff-top all have symbolic meanings.

the tissue paper. Leaf of this thinness is impossible to handle directly – if it is touched it will be quickly absorbed into the skin.

Some gold leaf is produced by beating machines that reproduce the motions of a skilled gold beater, but the highest quality of leaf, a mere 0.05 of a micron thick, is still produced by hand. This metal is thinner than the wavelength of visible light and is invisible when viewed from the edge.

THE GILDING PROCESS

Applying leaf to any surface to be gilded is a delicate job. The surface itself must be scrupulously clean and carefully primed so that it is both smooth and sealed. The surface is then given a coat of size, which is a

thin glue. The gold is placed on it while the size is still slightly sticky. Usually the gilder transfers the leaf to the receiving surface using a camel-hair brush, rubbing the brush over his or her hair to charge it with static electricity, as well as to pick up tiny traces of natural oil, which help the gold to stick to the brush. Once applied, the gold can either be burnished with soft cotton or given a more reflective surface by rubbing it with a tool tipped with a polished agate, which is used for burnishing and polishing. Surfaces that are too convoluted to be gilded with leaf can be covered with very fine gold powder suspended in an adhesive.

In medieval Europe, gold leaf was used in illuminated manuscripts, applied to ornate initial capitals and to the borders of the pages as well to the illustrations. It was similarly used to enrich paintings done on wooden or metal grounds, especially to depict haloes. Gold leaf was also used to decorate

the spines and covers of valuable books, and many of these exhibit artistry of the highest level. It is used today, of course, in the blocking of spine and title lettering on some hardback books.

GILDING LESSER METALS

Often an important part of the goldsmith's work has been to fix a thin layer of gold to the surface of items made from lesser metals. This has not always been a matter of deceit, some gilding has a highly practical purpose. Silver vessels, for example, can be attacked by the acids in wine, or even tea, which can impart a nasty taste. A thin layer of gold can protect such items, as well as the drinker, from damage.

For many centuries, the ability of mercury to combine with gold was widely used to gild silver and base metal items, the mercury being used as a medium to transfer the precious metal to the surface of less precious ones. If, for example, a metal worker wished to give a golden finish to a silver surface, the silver would first be rubbed all over with mercury. This action would cause the silver and mercury to become alloyed, producing silver amalgam at the surface. On to this amalgamated surface a layer of thin gold leaf would be laid and, in turn, the gold would amalgamate with the mercury to produce a new alloy of silver, gold and mercury. When the object was heated the mercury would boil away as vapour, leaving behind the silver covered with a coat of gold. The process could be repeated again and again, if necessary, until a substantial layer of gold was built up. Another method was for the goldsmith to make a gold amalgam and add this to the surface before heating the object to drive off the mercury, a process known as "fire gilding".

DEPLETION GILDING

Metal working in North and South America began as early as 2,000 BC, perhaps even before then. South American craftsmen invented many techniques used in other parts of the world. They cast complex pieces by the lost-wax process, formed masks and figurines by raising the metal from solid ingots, they soldered different pieces together, and decorated sheet gold with repoussé work. Their particular forte, however, was a way of gilding gold alloy objects so they appeared to be made of solid gold.

This form of gilding works not by adding gold to an object, but by removing base metal from the alloy. For this reason it is usually called depletion gilding. Spanish conquistadors often seized what appeared to be solid gold objects only to discover later that they were made of far less valuable tumbaga, an alloy of gold and copper, which had a gold surface.

The proportion of the two metals varied, but usually the copper formed about 20 percent. Silver was also often part of the alloy – not added deliberately but because it occurred naturally in the gold that was mined. Tumbaga was a key metal in South America: since tin was unknown to indigenous metal workers it was impossible for them to produce bronze, a copper-tin alloy, for weapons and tools as their Old World counterparts had done.

The first step in depletion gilding was to form the object in tumbaga, either by casting it, or by making it from sheet metal. When this was completed, the copper in the alloy which was nearest to the surface was converted into a copper compound, which was relatively easy to remove. The first stage in achieving this was to heat the object in air to turn the metallic copper at the surface to copper oxide. The copper oxide was next removed with an acid, perhaps that contained in urine or produced by crushing certain plants to extract their natural juices. To leach out the copper, the object, the acidic juice, salt and water were all boiled together. Exactly which plants were

Cast-gold umbrella tops are often ornate. The one opposite belongs to an Akoben chief; the one on this page is the symbol for the Kyidom clan.

interior alloy which is already rich in gold. Why then was it used? Two theories have been put forward. The first is that tumbaga was widely used in making "gold" objects because it is far easier to cast than either unalloyed gold or copper. A mixture of 20 percent copper and 80 percent gold melts at 911°C (1,672°F) compared to 1,063°C (1,945°F) for gold or 1,083°C (1,981°F) for copper in their pure forms. This lower temperature may have been important as pre-Columbian goldsmiths lacked one important piece of equipment that was available to metal-smiths in much of the rest of the world – they did not have bellows.

Obtaining the relatively high temperatures necessary for metal working is largely dependent on forcing air through burning fuel. Since South American metal workers did not have bellows, they had to make use of any air-flow that was available to get their fuel up to temperature – sometimes working on the windy tops of mountains – and themselves blowing air down hollow canes into their charcoal-burning braziers.

Pieces made in this way still had the disadvantage of tarnishing fairly readily because the copper at the surface would oxidize on exposure to air. Another probable reason then, was to give these easily cast tumbaga objects a corrosion-resistant surface.

used is not now certain but it has been plausibly suggested that the crucial acid was oxalic, as this can be derived from plants and is still used in Ecuador, mixed with salt and water, for cleaning jewellery. The depleting process may have been repeated several times to get the surface to the satisfaction of the goldsmith. Once that was achieved, and all the copper oxide removed by the acid, the goldsmith burnished the surface to give it a high polish and also to consolidate the relatively thin layer of the noble metal from which it was now made.

Depletion gilding, unlike fire gilding and other methods of adding an outer gold layer does not actually save much of the precious metal. While the other methods work by covering up less valuable base metals, depletion gilding only covers up an

The hieroglyphs on this Egyptian coin translate as "good gold". Perhaps this was one of the first hallmarks. The coin dates from c. 350 BC; the gold was probably from the Egyptian mines in Nubia.

ROLLED GOLD

A desire to make the most of any available gold is understandable: the material is precious and beyond the reach of many people. Pre-Columbian goldsmiths found ways to produce a gold surface on objects made of alloys and various forms of gilding have been used to make silver or base-metal objects appear to be solid gold. A third, far more recent, method involves fixing gold to a lesser metal to produce "rolled gold" or, as it is called in North America, "cased gold". This 19th-century method of fixing gold to a base metal could only have been invented once the steam engine had been developed, for it requires great energy to roll the two metals together under high pressure.

A sheet of carefully prepared gold, or gold alloy, and an equally smooth and clean sheet of backing metal – usually steel – are firmly clamped together, sometimes with a layer of silver solder between them, and heated to about 800°C (1,472°F) until they are firmly welded together. The two-metal sheet is now squeezed repeatedly between rollers until it is of the required thickness. This process, of course, produces material which can be seen to be gold on one face, steel on the other, but if gold is required on both faces, the steel can initially be sandwiched between two gold sheets and all three sheets rolled together.

Rolled gold is used for a variety of purposes, watch cases being a particularly popular one. Anything made of it has the advantage that its outer surfaces not only look splendid (and expensive) but are corrosion resistant: a rolled-gold watch case with a gold layer 20 microns thick is calculated to take about 20 years before the base metal begins to show.

The tumbaga lime flask of a seated female was made by casting the figure first and then, using depletion gilding, giving it a surface of gold. Dated AD 600–1100, it comes from Quimbaya (Colombia) where most items were made of tumbaga.

HALLMARKING

Because gold is so valuable, people must have confidence in its purity. This has been a concern of rulers down the ages, possibly on the basis that if any adulteration of the metal were to take place, it should be done under their control. In England, a system was created nearly 700 years ago to make sure

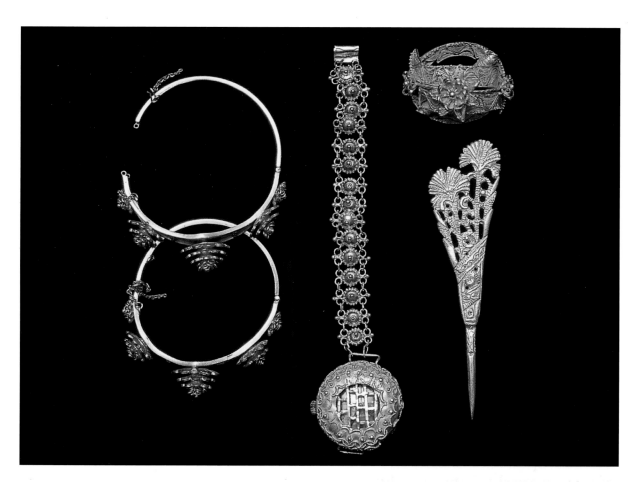

that gold objects met a standard of purity. In 1300, King Edward II established that gold objects should not be sold until they were tested by wardens of The Company of Goldsmiths and marked to show their purity. From this law there developed a system of hallmarking which has continued in Britain and has parallels all over the world. In Britain, all makers of gold objects are still required by law to submit them for this testing and marking before they can be sold.

The first English hallmark was a leopard's head and over time other marks were added to the repertoire, including the personal marks of individual makers, letters to indicate the year of marking, and signs for the various assay offices. An object which is hallmarked, or stamped, is one that has been subjected to an official assay, or test, to establish its degree of purity.

Hallmarks indicate where and when a piece was made as well as who made it. The symbols on the gold marked with the hallmark stamp above show that it is 9-karat gold and that it was tested in London in 1985.

The modern Ashanti jewellery, top, is marked with a hallmark that indicates important qualities to its buyer, especially its purity.

ASHANTI GOLD WORKING

"Some rings are of solid gold ornamented with various devices…others are composed entirely of network…The Ashantee artists are expert in moulding gold into the form of birds, fishes and animals."

The land that Europeans came to call the Gold Coast was not only a source of vast quantities of gold but also one of those special places where for centuries gold work of the very highest standard was produced. That tradition continues today and goldsmiths still make superb items of regalia and exquisite jewellery using techniques developed hundreds of years ago. We do not know exactly when gold working, and especially casting, began in the Akan forest zone but it was clearly well established by the time the Portuguese reached the coast by sea. In all probability, gold was being cast locally by the 14th century, perhaps even earlier. One day archaeological excavations may allow us to date its introduction accurately, but until then we can only speculate.

The Portuguese, landing on the coast in 1482 and coming from a country hungry for gold, described with awe – and greed – the appearance of the first local ruler they met: "his arms and legs and neck were covered with chains and trinkets of gold in many shapes, and many bells and large beads of gold were hanging from the hair of his bard and his head."

Some 300 years later, the same wonder at local gold work was evident in the description of the golden riches of Kumasi, the Ashanti capital, left us by the young Englishman Thomas Bowdich. As a member of a British embassy, he had been present at a dazzling reception mounted by the king and chiefs. Describing the magnificent attire of the chiefs, he

This gold casting was used to decorate the sheath of one of the Asantehene's state swords. Its design derives from an imported European lidded vessel.

noted, "a band of gold and beads encircled the knee, from which several strings of the same depended; small circles of gold like guineas, rings, and casts of animals were strung round their ankles…manillas and rude lumps of rock gold hung from their left wrists, which were so heavily laden as to be supported on the head of one of their most handsome boys. Gold and silver pipes and canes dazzled the eye in every direction. Wolves' and rams' heads, as large as life, cast in gold, were suspended from their gold-handled swords…" Back in London, a critic was later to dismiss Bowdich's account as an Arabian Nights fantasy.

CONSUMMATE CRAFTSMEN

If the gold of Kumasi was overwhelming beyond belief, time and time again Europeans also noted with awe the quantities of gold worn in other, less rich parts, of the Gold Coast. And the skills and creativity of local craftsmen were widely acknowledged by European visitors, even when they were happy to melt down the jewels they had obtained to turn them into bullion. Recent research has added to our appreciation of the abilities of these gold workers, abilities that are astounding when one takes into account what they used – little more than a few basic hand tools – to create masterworks. This disparity between the tools used and the achieved result can be explained by the high level of artistry and skill they have acquired over the centuries. If their methods of working have not changed greatly over time, it is because they are perfectly suited to their purpose.

THE GOLDEN STOOL

Goldsmiths played an important role in the growth of Ashanti political control in the 18th and 19th centuries. The golden objects they created served to distinguish the various ranks of chieftainship, indicated the particular functions of court officials and even helped to decide whether there should be war or peace. It is no exaggeration to say that without gold regalia the Ashanti Empire simply could not have functioned. And, of course, at the very hub of the whole Ashanti political system was the ultimate gold creation, the Golden Stool of Ashanti, or *Sika 'dwa Kofi*, which actually means "the Golden Stool created on a Friday". According to Ashanti legend, at the beginning of the 17th century the great priest Anokye brought this stool down from the heavens. It settled on the knees of the seated king, Asantehene Osei Tutu. From that time onwards, the Golden Stool was prized above all other items of regalia and no royal candidate could truly assume kingship until he had possession of it. Today, the Ashanti believe the Golden Stool contains the soul of their nation and they see it as providing the essential link that joins all stages of their history together.

"GOLD IS KING"

There were several reasons for the flaunting of vast quantities of gold at Ashanti courts. Most important was the desire to impress the populace, rivals, visitors and outsiders with wealth and power. The Ashanti have a saying "*sike ne ohene*", meaning "gold is king". Political power and the possession and display of wealth are inextricably bound together in Ashanti society. Items of gold regalia also served as reminders of important events in the state's history and in the career of its ruler or his predecessors. Some items may have been trophies seized from defeated enemy states, others may have been copies of coveted items once possessed by slain rivals. Sometimes an object was made specifically to commemorate a slain

The King of Ashanti, Otumfuo Opoku Ware II, is carried in his palanquin surrounded by state swords, above, and sits in state on the right. The Golden Stool resting on the black chair beside him represents the soul of the Ashanti

enemy: today, there hangs from the Golden Stool an effigy of a man wearing a coat and cocked hat and bearing a sword. It represents Sir Charles MacCarthy, the British governor killed in battle by the Ashanti in 1824.

Items of regalia also had a diplomatic function. As new areas were absorbed into the Ashanti Empire the Asantehenes sent them to their new vassal chiefs to cement their allegiance and strengthen their loyalty. At the same time, such gifts helped absorb the new provinces into a common system of symbolism.

The Ashanti goldsmiths are supreme masters of casting gold by the *cire perdue*, or lost-wax, process. This is how they made – and still make – the rings that adorned the fingers and toes of their kings and chiefs, their armlets and bracelets, their pendants and pectorals, the motifs that they fastened to sandals and head bands, and the decorations on their sword

sheaths. Yet they are also experts in the far older and simpler technique of cold-working gold which, as the name suggests, does not require heat. This includes the shaping of gold by hammering and bending, and the cutting, incising and punching of it to give a form of raised decoration called repoussé.

COLD GOLD

Cold-working gold involves first making sheets of gold, which is not a difficult process. Nuggets, or a mixture of nuggets and dust melted together to make larger pieces, can be hammered out to produce thick or thin sheets of foil. Much of the gold found in the Ashanti area contains only tiny proportions of other metals naturally alloyed with it, so it is easy to work by hammering.

Relatively thick gold foil was used principally on objects created for the royal court. Its most common use was to cover wooden carvings, giving them a brilliant surface that reflected the bright rays of the tropical sun by day and caught the flickering gleam of oil lamps by night. The court objects adorned in this way were dazzling in appearance and served as a continual visual reminder of the wealth and power of the Ashanti rulers and those in their service.

Other objects treated in this way included the handles of curved-bladed swords which, at least by the 17th century, had ceased to be used as weapons and were used instead as symbols of high office. The most important of these swords, decorated with elaborate gold castings, were the ones on which the most senior chiefs swore their allegiance to the Asantehene when they were installed in office. The great oath swords were held to be particularly powerful and sacred and the men whose duty it was to carry them wore a distinctive head dress with a great fan of eagle feathers springing from the top and a pair of gold ram's horns at the front. Usually these horns were cast in gold but occasionally they were carved from wood and then covered with gold foil.

Lesser swords of various kinds were carried by royal servants, sometimes being used to prove that they were official emissaries of the court. Their wooden handles, in the shape of two spheres joined by a cylinder, rather like a dumb-bell, were decorated by covering them with gold foil. A third, very large and unusual kind of sword had three blades set at equal angles to each other and three handles decorated with thick gold foil. Swords like this stood on the ground, handles uppermost, near a monarch when he sat in judgement. They seem to have been made in this especially large and elaborate form to impress supplicants and visitors with the king's power.

GLORIOUS UMBRELLAS

Many gold-decorated items are intended to be highly visible, even from a considerable distance, standing out in great parades or from the turmoil of the battlefield, for example. Among the most spectacular and noticeable items of court art are the umbrella tops. These carved wooden finials, covered entirely with gold sheet or, in a few cases, with sheets of silver, are some 30–60 cm (1–2 ft) in height. They crown the domes of the huge umbrellas that shade rulers when they appear in public. The umbrellas, which may be 3.5 m (12 ft) or more in diameter, are usually made of patterned cloth edged with a bright red valance. At appropriate moments, they are danced up and down so that the valances swirl, creating a cooling breeze.

The finials incorporate the combined skills of the goldsmith and the woodcarver. The latter carves the underlying form – war horn, elephant, bird, and so on – and carefully shapes the socket in the base by

The Asantehemaa, the Queen Mother of the Ashantis, top right, sits in the Seko, or armchair, which signifies her supreme position in the Ashanti traditional system. At a durbar, the royal women of Ghana, including Queen Mothers from local and district households, seated right, are adorned with gold ornaments.

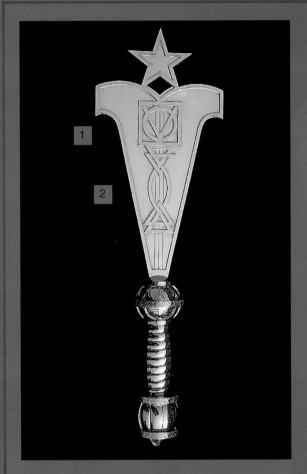

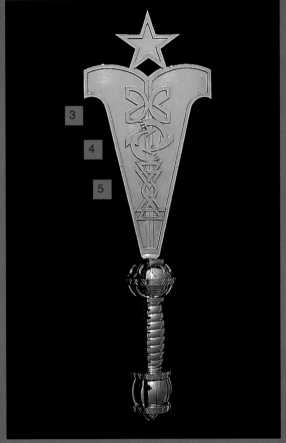

The State Sword is a symbol of the authority of the President of the Republic of Ghana but its origin is deeply rooted in the Akan tradition of kingship authority. The President holds the Sword in his right hand when he takes the Oath of Office at his inauguration. It is also borne before him when he comes to the National Assembly for the State Opening of Parliament.

Every Chief in the Akan Traditional Area, which covers most of Ghana and parts of La Côte d'Ivoire, has a Sword that symbolizes the authority of his position. When Ghana gained independence from Colonial rule and established parliamentary democracy, the Nkrumah government of the First Republic felt it was both fitting and becoming that the Ghanaian symbol of authority vested in the traditional rulers be incorporated in the new parliamentary democracy, which all parties had agreed to establish in Ghana. The double-bladed State Sword is made of pure Ghanaian gold and was specially designed to incorporate Adinkra symbols that are rich in meaning and symbolism.

Sword Key
The Ghana Star at the top of the sword represents the unity of the nation and the lodestar of African freedom.
1 Nyame-tum *symbolizes the sovereignty of God over society.*
2 and 5 The Adehye-borobe, *or pineapple, signifies both royalty and sovereignty.*
3 Fawobo *is the traditional symbol of freedom.*
4 Bi-nka-bi *is the symbol for justice.*

The State Sword and Mace

The Mace is a symbol of authority in the Ghanaian Parliament. It is entrusted solely to the Speaker, whose daily procession into the Chamber is led by the Marshal with the Mace. This event signifies the ceremonial opening of each Sitting day in the House.

The Marshal carries the Mace into Parliament on his right shoulder and places it in a special holder in front of the Clerk's Table, where it remains throughout the Sitting as a symbol of Parliamentary authority.

which it is fixed to the umbrella. The goldsmith hammers out the gold into thin flexible sheets and then forms it around the wood, fixing it permanently in place with tiny staples. There is some evidence to suggest that in their earliest form these umbrella finials were objects such as the skulls of slain animals, but by 1817 the majority of them seem to have been gold-covered carvings.

Spokesmen's staffs

Another important and spectacular item of regalia covered with sheet gold was the special staff carried by the king's spokesmen and advisers, his *akyeame* (singular *okyeame*). The job of the *okyeame* is to speak in public for the king, interpreting his decisions and comments to his people. He is also responsible for repeating and clarifying the speeches of those who appear before the king and for advising the ruler on his decisions. He is required to remember all relevant precedents and recall earlier cases and testimonies. Ultimately he is responsible for all publicly conveyed decisions and, if a monarch is judged to be in error, it is always the *okyeame* who is held to be at fault.

The finials on the spokesmen's staffs indicate their rank. Today the staffs are elaborately carved along their length with knots, swirls and a variety of complex patterns and motifs. Usually they are made in two or three sections that fit neatly together with rod and socket joints, culminating in their most striking feature, a large, carved finial. Perhaps 30 cm (1 ft) or more in height, it may depict animals, humans or significant objects, or all three in combination. Like much of the gold work made for the court, these are not just strikingly attractive objects – they also have a deeper, proverbial significance.

These staffs have grown more and more elaborate over time although, like umbrella finials, they have only been completely covered with gold in the last two centuries or so. Spokesmen's staffs were originally derived from the gold- and silver-headed

canes that European traders and governors offered to their local allies as tokens of peace and friendship.

Early locally made "canes" had simple cylindrical tops covered with gold sheet and were decorated with floral patterns copied from imported European metalware and ceramics. By 1817, the royal spokesmen had long staffs covered in their entirety with gold foil; however, the elaborate finials are almost entirely a 20th-century development.

DECORATING WITH PUNCHES

The decorative patterns worked on the surface of sheet gold were made by two distinct processes that Ashanti metal workers often used in combination. They punched out the surface of the gold from the back and then cut or punched into it from the front. When working from the back, the smith mostly used small, specially made brass or iron punches, each tipped with a particular design such as a circle, rectangle or crescent. Patterns were formed by the repeated punching of the design into the metal. Once the sheet was turned over, these patterns were revealed as raised areas on the outer surface of the gold. However, to sharpen the design, the goldsmith might then work it over from the front, emphasizing the raised areas by outlining them with a series of dots or lines. This was done by pressing or gently hammering a pointed piece of metal into the gold, or by cutting into it slightly with the tip of a blade.

These two cold-working techniques were widely used in Ashanti and can also be seen on items such as the rectangular casings made to contain the talismans attached to royal sandals, head bands and even to their war robes. Sheet gold with this sort of repoussé work was also used to adorn the personal stools of the Asantehene and the Queen Mother. Thin gold sheet with repoussé decoration was also used on the small egg-timer-shaped wooden stands, on which the king's dishes were placed at meal times.

The Atumtufuo, *or gun-bearers, above, are each carrying a gun to represent all the past kings as well as the present king. They also carry sets of gold-covered knives on their backs.*

Ashanti gold features heavily at state occasions, right. Clockwise from the top: the Paramount Chief of Agogo and his retinue; court criers, who keep order at state functions; the Golden Stool carried by the official stool carrier; official sandal carriers; the bearer of the sword used in swearing allegiance to the Asantehene.

The interplay of an exquisite kente cloth and gold ornaments portray the dignity of a Ghanaian chief, left. A variety of state umbrellas are used by chiefs who have permission to do so, above. Not all chiefs are entitled to use them.

A close up of an umbrella reveals its amazing gold top, top right. Each insignia has a special meaning and easily identifies the position of each chief. The linguists below right also belong to various chiefs. Their staffs represent their authority.

Gold was sometimes wrapped over small wooden carvings, which were attached to the hats; sometimes the gold sheet was cut out into elaborate strips that were sewn to the leather. Court messengers or criers had hats with elaborate rectangular gold-covered plaques at the front, and many chiefs wore thin strips of coloured velvet or silk around their foreheads, which were embellished with small wooden motifs covered with thin gold sheet.

One of the most spectacular of all the items of regalia decorated with sheet gold is the Golden Axe of Ashanti, a symbolic iron-bladed axe enclosed in a leopard-skin sheath, elaborately decorated with both cast and sheet gold. The axe was formerly sent with royal emissaries on major diplomatic missions. Its design combined the rich brightness of gold with the yellow and black of the leopard skin. Like the elephant, the leopard was a royal beast and a symbol of royal power and ferocity.

CAST GOLD

The craftsmen of Ashanti are most celebrated as casters of gold and other metals. Their superb skills are to be seen in two fields, namely the gold jewels and decorations created for their rulers and the brass weights made for measuring units of gold dust for trading. The same basic casting techniques were used in each case, but whereas only the most high-ranking people in Ashanti society could adorn themselves with gold, everyone needed brass weights to measure out the gold dust that served as the local currency.

Gold was cast by Ashanti goldsmiths into a wide variety of forms including armlets, anklets, rings, beads, pectoral discs, sandal adornments, bells and decorations for the sheaths of state swords. Castings ranged in size from a few millimetres (one-tenth of

an inch) to 8 cm (3 inches) in length. All these items of gold work, however, were made in the same way. The object was first made in beeswax and then reproduced in metal using the lost-wax, or *cire perdue,* process.

THE LOST-WAX TECHNIQUE

In theory, the basic lost-wax technique is very simple: the craftsman first makes an object in wax and then converts the wax object into metal. This is done by shrouding the wax with clay and allowing this clay encasement, or "investment", to dry out and harden. The clay and the wax model it contains are then heated until the wax melts and runs away, either by soaking into the clay or by dribbling out of a hole made through it, known as a sprue hole. When the wax has gone it leaves behind a cavity of its original shape in the clay. Molten metal is then poured into this cavity. The metal cools and solidifies in the exact shape of the original wax model. The clay is then broken and the casting removed and cleaned up. This is the basic process

but it must be used with great skill if good results are to be achieved. Its great advantage is that it allows a craftsman to work initially in wax, a material that is easy to manipulate and shape. It can be moulded or carved, rolled into fine sheets or threads. If mistakes are made, the wax can simply be re-heated and re-shaped until the craftsman is satisfied. Only when everything is exactly right in inexpensive wax does the more expensive and complicated process begin.

The wax typically came from the hives of wild bees either from the rain forest or from the drier savannah lands to the north. It was first purified by pounding it and then boiling it in water. The molten wax floated to the top and was skimmed off. It was then melted again and filtered through a cloth into water to set.

A number of refinements to the basic lost-wax process have been developed and are used by Ashanti gold workers. One of these is to attach one or more wax rods to the original model so that, when it is encased in clay, the rod goes right through the clay and sticks out. When it is heated, the rod melts,

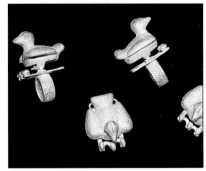

Ashanti craftsmen are expert casters specializing in the lost-wax process. The outer clay covering looks black because of the finely ground charcoal that is mixed into it. This helps the gold to stay molten and to disperse any trapped air. The final objects, beautiful gold Ashanti rings, are a testimony to the type of skill required to produce them.

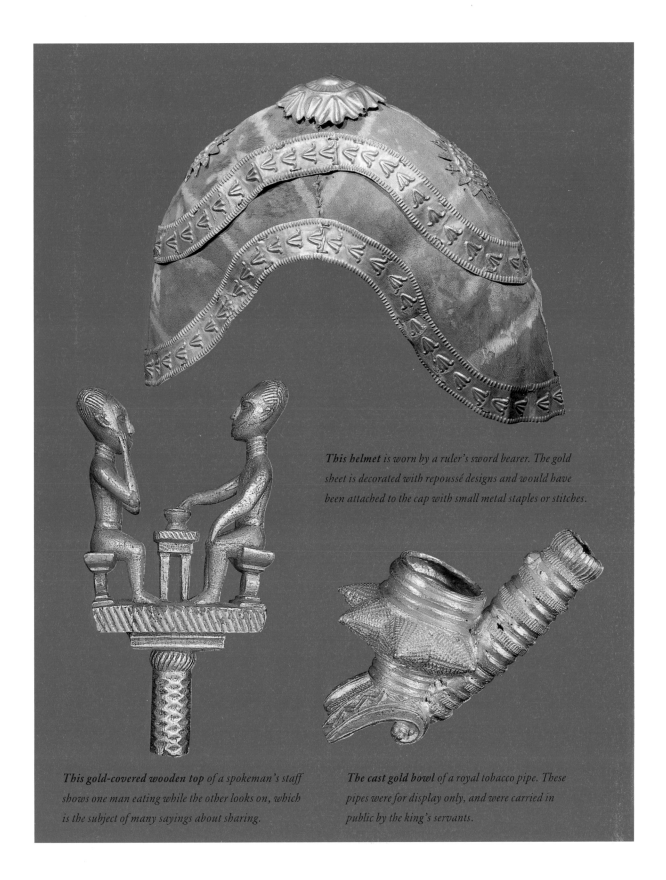

*This **helmet** is worn by a ruler's sword bearer. The gold sheet is decorated with repoussé designs and would have been attached to the cap with small metal staples or stitches.*

*This **gold-covered wooden top** of a spokeman's staff shows one man eating while the other looks on, which is the subject of many sayings about sharing.*

*The **cast gold bowl** of a royal tobacco pipe. These pipes were for display only, and were carried in public by the king's servants.*

leaving a short tube, or sprue hole, in the clay, through which the rest of the molten wax trickles out. The sprue also serves as the channel through which the molten metal is introduced into the cavity left behind by the lost-wax model.

TOOLS OF THE TRADE

Ashanti goldsmiths used very simple tools in shaping beeswax. They included a long wooden block with a smooth surface, a flat strip of smooth wood rather like the blade of a palette knife, another strip of smooth wood with a point at one or both ends, one or two small blades and a thin pointed rod of iron. The flat wooden block was used for rolling out strips of wax, the blades for carving it and the pointed spatula for modelling it, cutting grooves into it, and for picking out detail. The thin iron rod, when heated, could be used to cut into the wax or to melt one area so that a small piece of wax would stick to it. Many goldsmiths also used a small brass lamp consisting of an open-topped square reservoir for oil on a cylindrical column. The corners of the reservoir were pinched together to hold wicks of cotton. These lamps provided heat for softening wax and, when used with a blow pipe, for soldering together tiny pieces of gold. Ashanti goldsmiths use these same simple yet effective tools today.

THE LOST-BEETLE TECHNIQUE

Ashanti goldsmiths also practised a casting technique rarely, if ever, found elsewhere. Considerable numbers of their brass goldweights were made in this way, which involved casting a real object rather than a wax model. Sometimes known as the lost-beetle technique, it involved building up a clay mould around a suitable small object such as a beetle, small fruit, flower, seed or groundnut and affixing a wax sprue rod to it. The mould was then heated in the same way as for a wax model. At a high enough temperature the encased object turned to dust and,

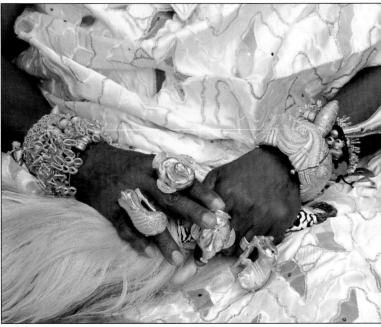

As part of the 25th anniversary celebrations of the enstoolment of Otumfuo Opoku Ware II, the King of the Ashantis, ceremonies were held throughout the Ashanti region, at which Ashanti finery and jewellery were displayed in all their glory. Many of the gold trinkets belong to a stool and must be passed down the generations.

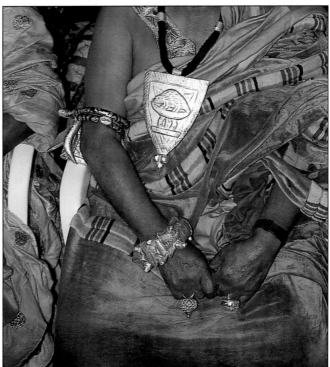

eventually, molten brass could be cast in the cavity. Most likely this was done as a *jeu d'esprit* and a demonstration of ingenuity.

HOLLOW CASTING

The Ashanti had vast amounts of gold but they used it economically. Most of the castings made for their kings and chiefs were not solid gold; they were hollow. Making a hollow object is a four-stage process. The first stage is to make a core that temporarily forms the heart of the object and will be removed later to create a hollow centre.

If an Ashanti goldsmith were casting a human head, for example, the core would be constructed out of a mixture of finely ground clay and charcoal. The goldsmith would shape this mixture into the general form and size of the required head and leave it to dry out completely. Over this core a layer of wax would then be applied. Usually this layer of wax would not cover the core completely and parts at the back would be left without a wax covering.

On the front surface of the wax the craftsman would build up the facial features, the eyes, lips, nose, mouth, hair, and so on. When this second stage was completed the craftsman would attach wax rods to the head and cover it completely with several layers of clay. This covering, of course, would stick to, or fuse with, the core in the places where it was not covered by wax. Once the covering was dry the wax would be melted out and the core held in place where it had fused with it.

The molten metal would next be poured into the head-shaped cavity that the wax had left behind when it was "lost" by melting it. When the mould was broken away the gold head would, of course, be wrapped around the core in the areas where the wax had previously covered it but, in those parts where it

The children below are imitating court criers and sword bearers. The head gear, or tekua, *on the right is adorned with gold trinkets and is worn on various ceremonial occasions.*

was not covered, the core would still be visible and accessible. The final stage, therefore, was to carefully pick out the core from the inside of the casting to make it hollow. An examination of many Ashanti castings from the 19th century shows that they were made in this way.

The majority of pectoral or 'kra discs were made by gold casting, although some were made from gold sheet and decorated with repoussé work. The name for these discs comes from the word *okra*, the name given to one of the key royal officials. The *okra* was a man or boy who had a special ritual role as the "soul of the king", but who also performed a number of functions around the court. An *okra*, whether at court or when dispatched on official business, wore a circular disc on his chest, suspended by a white cord usually made from pineapple leaf fibre.

Some of the most exquisite 'kra pectoral discs consist of a central raised conical boss joined to a rim by intricate openwork patterns made up of thin gold filaments. The rim itself curves round about half a centimetre (a quarter of an inch) at the back but the rest of the rear of the disc is open. An initial core would have been made in the form of a disc with smoothly bevelled edge. On this, the central boss was modelled in wax and then a rim was modelled around the front and back of the edge. Thin threads of wax were then laid on the front surface of the core only, joining the rim to the boss. After sprue rods had been fixed to the rim, and the wax invested and the disc cast in the normal way, the core disc was removed to leave a delicate tracery of unsupported gold threads holding the boss and rim together. Many of the rosette, star, moon and floral motifs that decorate royal sandals and head bands were also cast in the same way.

A chief and a member of his royal family from a Traditional Area of the Ashanti region must display their wealth according to their position and tradition, below left. The Procession of Chiefs and their retinue pictured below right comprises both young and old sword-bearers.

PRECISION CASTING

Many Ashanti castings in both brass and gold are distinguished by their great delicacy and the quantity and precision of the detail they show. Some have found it hard to believe that this was achieved by such simple techniques. It has even been suggested that Ashanti goldsmiths swung their moulds and molten gold around their heads at the end of a rope so that the gold was driven by centrifugal force into the tiniest details in the mould. Although modern Western jewellers and technicians use centrifuges in this way to cast items when great precision is necessary, the Ashanti never did. They achieved their superb results far more easily and safely, without whizzing containers of molten gold around their heads.

The precision of Ashanti gold work can be attributed partly to their use of substantial quantities of charcoal in the investment. The original wax model was initially covered with a very thin paste made up almost entirely of extremely finely ground charcoal suspended in water. The goldsmith, usually using the tip of a chicken feather, covered the wax model with this paste, being careful to leave no area, however tiny, where the paste did not adhere. The model was then put to one side and the paste allowed to dry. This process was repeated until several layers had been applied, the later ones containing increasing proportions of fine-ground clay mixed in with the charcoal. Once these were dry, the final covering of the wax model was applied, but this time the clay had little or no charcoal in it.

The importance of the charcoal was twofold. First, the very fine powder could cover and enclose every detail, however delicate, of the wax model. Second, during the actual casting, the charcoal served to absorb any gases given off as the metal and the mould were heated up. It also acted as a good insulator, and therefore helped the molten metal to retain its heat. This was important because the gold, once it was melted, had to stay molten and fully liquid as it was poured into the mould if the casting was to be successful. If bubbles of air or other gases were trapped either in the metal or in the space it was intended to fill, the casting would have been faulty. Similarly, if the metal began to cool and harden too soon, the mould would not be filled. The presence of the charcoal-rich investment both prevented bubbles from forming and kept the metal from cooling too quickly.

The basic need to make sure the gold or brass stayed fully liquid for a time was aided by an additional refinement in gold casting used by the Ashanti. This involved enclosing the metal in a shallow clay cup, which was attached to the mould at a point over the sprue hole. The mould and the cup containing the metal were cemented together with wet clay and this bond was allowed to dry. Then they were put into the hottest part of the furnace, mould uppermost, until the goldsmith was certain that the metal in the cup was completely molten. By this point, of course, the mould itself, the cup and the gold it contained, would all be at the same temperature – a temperature that was above the melting point of gold.

Then came the crucial moment, when all efforts would either be wasted or rewarded. The goldsmith carefully took the mould in a pair of tongs and rapidly inverted it so that the cup and its contents of molten gold was now at the top. The gold rushed into the space left by the lost wax and, if the craftsman had judged his quantity correctly, filled the space exactly, with a little remaining in the sprue tube, just to be sure. Because of the charcoal, and because all the elements were at the same high temperature, the gold stayed liquid and was not blocked by bubbles that would have prevented it from entirely filling the mould.

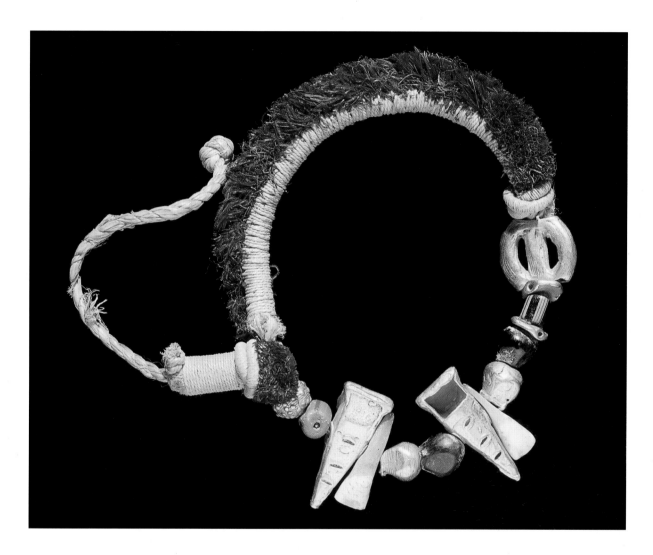

After a few minutes the mould was lifted from the furnace and allowed to cool. As the clay had been exposed to such high temperatures it had become a fairly tough piece of pottery, far harder than ordinary domestic Ashanti pottery. Once cool, the mould was broken open by one or more hard blows from a hammer. The casting was taken out and scrubbed to remove any remaining pieces of clay. In the past, castings were then boiled up in a special mixture containing red earth, which left a very fine deposit on the metal, giving it a distinctive red glow. It is interesting to note that one careful observer and eager inquirer into Ashanti technology described this casting process in detail in 1817. The very same

This protective talisman is made from vegetable fibre and includes glass beads and gold castings, some of which represent human teeth. It would have been worn around the owner's wrist.

processes are still being followed, to the letter, in Ashanti today.

THE GOLDSMITH'S WORKSHOP

Ashanti goldsmiths are always men. Because of religious beliefs to do with fertility, women are not allowed to model clay in any form – human or otherwise. In Kumasi, the Ashanti capital, goldsmiths traditionally congregated together in the part of the town called Adum where they were under

a measure of royal control and supervision. In other large towns, especially the capitals of the states in the Ashanti Confederation, it is also likely that there were goldsmiths' quarters. Traditionally, goldsmiths worked in or near their own homes, which were usually a group of rectangular rooms arranged on three or four sides around a small courtyard. In some cases they worked within this courtyard, perhaps sheltering from the fierce tropical sun in the shade of a tree or under a flimsy open-sided shelter made with a leaf thatch. Alternatively, they might set aside a work area behind or beside their house, again with some sort of shelter.

Now, as in the past, two things are essential to the goldsmith's workshop: a small shady area where he can create and safely lay out the various stages of his work as each is completed, and a furnace in which he can heat and melt gold in order to cast it into new forms. The furnace is critically important as it has to produce temperatures of over 1,000°C (1,832°F) in order to melt the gold. Until recently the Ashanti furnace was built of clay and fuelled with charcoal. Today, an old oil drum is sometimes used, lined with clay or, more rarely, with cement. Holes are punched through the sides near the bottom so that air can be blown from bellows into the burning charcoal. The traditional furnace was basically cylindrical, rather like a stout, thick-walled chimney, perhaps 1 m (3 ft) in height with a central shaft. Near the base were one or more holes leading into the shaft. The shaft was filled with charcoal, which was sometimes mixed with oily palm nut shells that produce an intense heat when they burn. The charcoal was ignited and air from bellows, probably pumped by the goldsmith's apprentices, was forced through the holes near the bottom of the shaft, driving oxygen through the charcoal and creating high temperatures.

Originally the bellows used would have been of the African type. The simplest of these was a bag made of animal skin with a hollow wooden tube tied in at one end. As the operator pulled up on the top of the bag, air was drawn in. When the bag was squashed down air was forced down the tube and into the furnace. Another form of bellows consisted of a drumlike wooden or clay cylinder with a loose sheet of skin tied around the top and a hollow tube inserted in its base. Similarly, when this skin was pulled up and then pushed down, air was driven out through a hole at the base of the drum and into the pipe. These bellows were normally used in pairs and, in the hands of strong and experienced operators, they could produce the powerful blasts of air needed to create the high temperatures necessary for smelting iron and other metals including gold, copper, brass and bronze. Gold Coast goldsmiths, however, were happy to adopt European-style bellows once these were introduced into the region. We know that this was the case because many of them were reproduced as gold-weights, as were other tools used by Ashanti metal workers, such as hammers and the tongs they used for lifting moulds in and out of the furnace.

THE GOLD CULTURE

The gold trade was one of the driving forces behind the growth of the Ashanti kingdom, and it was essential that control of the smiths who could work it was maintained. By tradition, when a rival group was defeated by the emerging Ashanti state, their specialist craftsmen were seized and transported to Kumasi where they were set to work for the Asantehene. Thus some of the Kumasi

These extremely complex castings are discs worn around the neck by young men who are servants of the Asantehene.

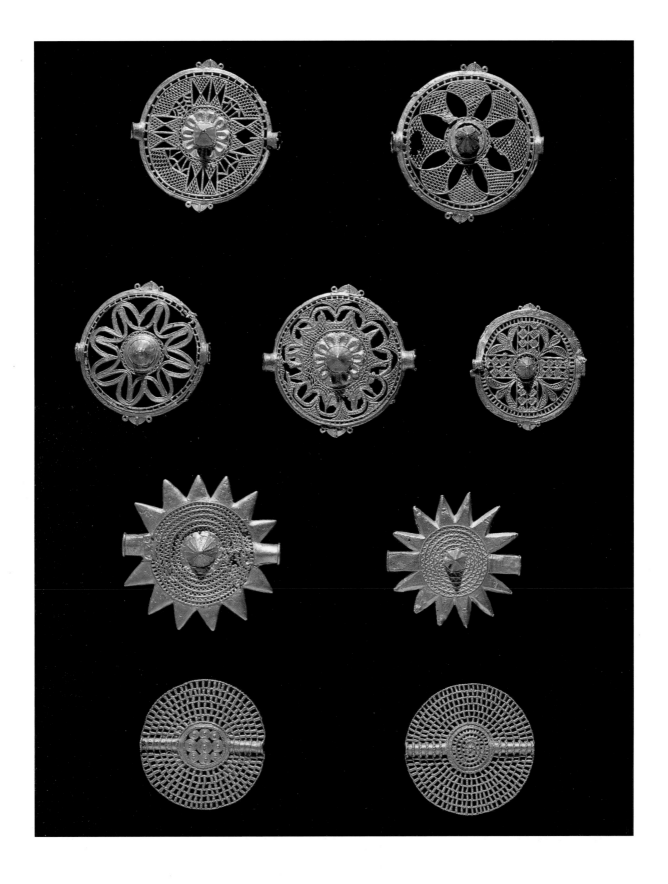

goldsmiths came from Tekyiman, probably in around 1720–30, and another group came after the defeat of Denkyira at the start of the 18th century. Once established in Kumasi, royal control was exercised over who they could work for and over what they could make.

We do not know how many goldsmiths there were in the major towns at the height of the Ashanti Empire but there must have been considerable numbers for, as we have seen, they were not only required to make gold objects for the rulers but also to cast brass vessels and the small brass weights used in trading with the local gold dust currency. Some idea of their numbers is, however, given by a survey made in 1909, that is, 13 years after the British had seized the Asantehene Prempeh I and forced him into exile in the Seychelles, and when the traditional political system in which goldsmiths had played a major role was much decayed. This survey indicated that there were no less than 89 goldsmiths in or around Kumasi. It is likely, though, that there were many more

The great sword below is called mpomponsuo, *and on it oaths of loyalty were sworn to the king of Ashanti. It is decorated with leopard skin as well as gold and silver sheet. It is the original sword made for Asantehene Opoku Ware I by the famous fetish priest Okomfo Anokye. The detail on the right is a hollow gold casting of a snake, perhaps a Gaboon viper, gripping an antelope.*

goldsmiths than this in Kumasi before the chaos and disintegration of the Ashanti kingdom in the closing decades of the 19th century.

STATUS SYMBOLS

Throughout the Ashanti kingdom there were, in theory at least, laws about who could possess gold and how much of it would be forfeit to the state on their death. Broadly speaking, status and gold went together. Both male and female slaves were not allowed to possess any gold ornaments; commoners could only keep gold dust. If they found nuggets in the course of mining or panning, they were to hand them over to their senior local chief. In return they would be given gold dust to the equivalent of a third of their value. All nuggets over 225 g (8 oz) in weight were claimed as the property of the king.

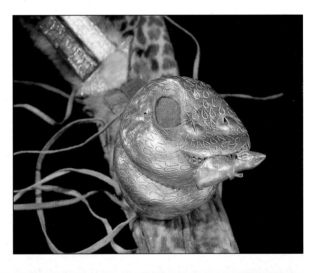

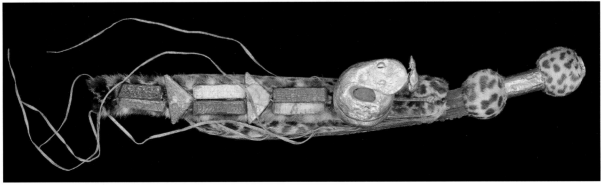

There were also controls over the types of regalia and their elaborateness that were permitted to be worn by chiefs at each level of the political hierarchy. The items worn by the Asantehene or carried by his servants set a pattern; any chief attempting to copy them without the Asantehene's permission was, in effect, challenging his power. Similarly, within each state in the Ashanti Confederacy, senior chiefs strove to distinguish themselves from the lesser chiefs who served them.

The Kumasi goldsmiths were directly overseen by one of the king's office holders, the *Eburahene*, or chief of hearths and furnaces, and they could only work for other chiefs with the king's permission. Nor were they trusted to be honest in other ways. The king's goldsmiths would make new items of regalia for him, and mend or rework existing ones and they were given little opportunity to profit from the occasion. When they were issued with gold from the royal treasury it was carefully weighed out and, it is said, their work was checked each day to make sure that none of it had been diverted for their personal use. Similarly, old items given them to be melted down and re-cast were weighed by court officials, both before and after casting, so that all of gold was accounted for.

Gold dust was used exclusively in trading and no other currencies, such as the cowrie, had any place in Ashanti commerce. Nuggets, that prerogative of kingship, were, of course, of no use in commercial transactions. The king's goldsmiths not only made exquisite gold objects, they had to make gold dust

This executioner's knife is copied from an imported European knife. It is fitted into a leather sheath and decorated with gold sheet. The attachments are local copies of the imported forms.

as well. The French trader Marie Joseph Bonnat (who was to become the first European to obtain a gold-mining concession on the Gold Coast) observed, while held captive in Kumasi in the early 1870s, the process by which nuggets were converted to the more useful gold dust.

Nuggets and ingots of gold were melted with red earth and sand in pottery crucibles. When the metal had become molten it was shaken vigorously so the two substances became mixed and then the mixture was flung into a container of cold water with which a little red earth had been mixed. This process had the effect of initially dispersing the molten metal among the sand and earth and then solidifying it into small grains in the water. Bonnat noted there were a hundred men employed exclusively on this work.

It was possible to use the tiniest specks of gold to carry out the most minor transaction, one or two grains being transferred on the tip of a knife blade if need be. People were obviously very careful to weigh gold dust accurately and to make sure that they got the exact amount they were owed.

Brass weights

Goldsmiths were also responsible for making the brass gold-weights for which Ashanti is justly famous. Almost everyone who is interested in African cultures knows of these small castings of animals, objects and situations from Ashanti life, often depicted with great wit and a delightful sharpness of observation. Although these representational weights are eagerly collected today they were outnumbered in the past by the simpler geometric weights, including discs, pyramids and rectangles, which were often decorated on one face with low-relief designs.

Brass weights were cast in their thousands by goldsmiths. Everyone involved in trade needed them

Peggy Appiah, *daughter of the late Sir Stafford Cripps, Chancellor of the Exchequer in Britain's postwar Labour government, and part of her huge collection of gold-weights, gold-dust boxes and* kuduo. *She is the custodian of one of the largest collections of Ashanti gold-weights in the world.*

as part of the basic equipment needed for weighing and checking the gold dust proffered in payment for goods. The essential tools for trading were one or more sets of simple balance scales, weights of known value, one or more spoons to transfer gold dust into the scale pans and a special scoop used to check for any lighter impurities. Most people also had one or more brass boxes in which they kept their gold carefully tied up in a scrap of cloth.

Usually all these essential trading tools were kept bundled up in a large piece of skin or cloth. A few of these bundles, called *futuo*, have survived more or less intact today, even though they were probably last used over 100 years ago. Surviving *futuo* contain two or three sets of scales as well as brass weights representing all the main units of the system, either singly or in

combination. They also contain one or more touchstones to test the purity of any large lumps of gold, usually several spoons of different sizes and the large open-ended scooplike utensil, a *famfa*.

TRICKS OF THE TRADE

All traders tried to protect themselves from being cheated, which suggests that most traders also tried to cheat. Cheating in the gold trade could be done in a variety of ways. One was by using adulterated gold,

Brass boxes *were used for storing twists of cloth that contained gold dust. Some would have been cast by the lost-wax process, others made from soldered riveted sheet brass.*

which was gold dust mixed with brass filings or gold alloyed with copper or brass and then filed to reduce it to inferior gold dust. Such attempts could sometimes be detected by the naked eye but, for the most part, in the myriad tiny specks of gold small colour differences were hard or impossible to spot.

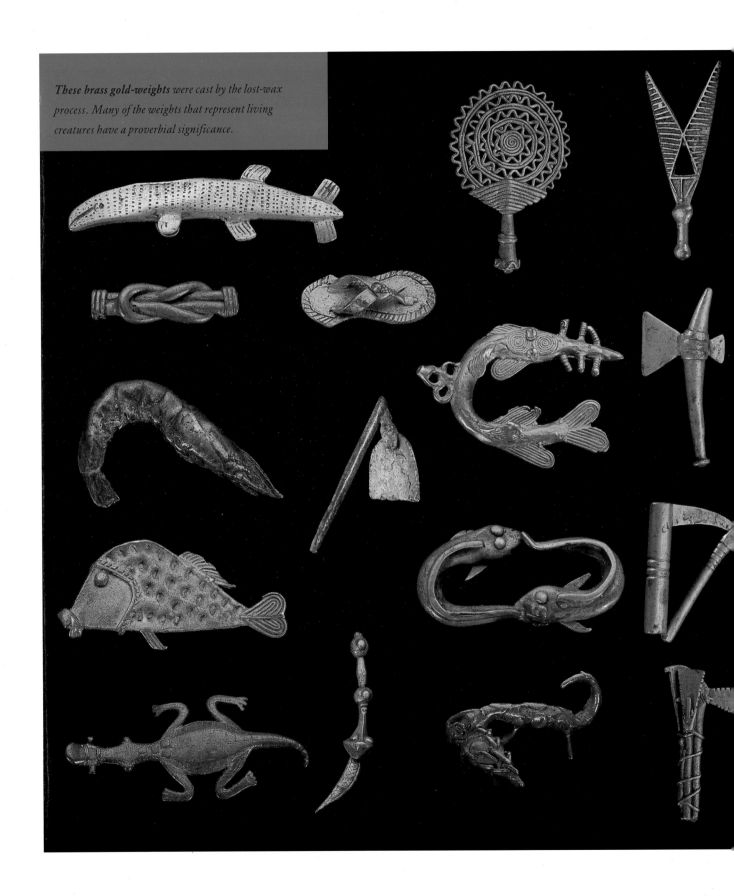

These brass gold-weights were cast by the lost-wax process. Many of the weights that represent living creatures have a proverbial significance.

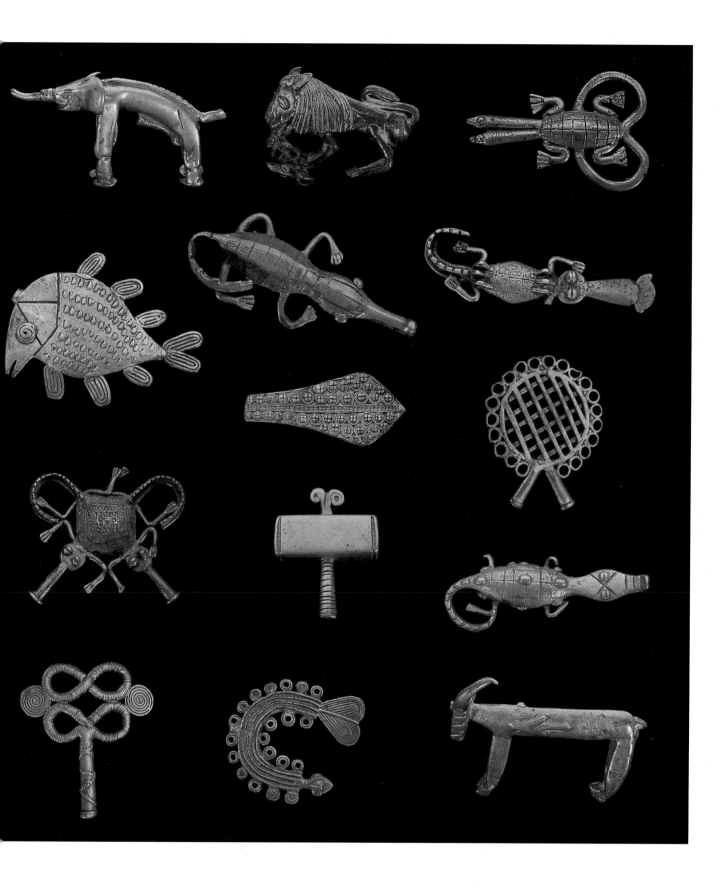

The *famfa* was used to reveal inferior or adulterated dust. The dust was placed in the bowl area and the user blew across it, driving it towards the open end. The pure gold, being heaviest, moved least, while brass, dirt or inferior gold was driven up to the open part from where it could be brushed away.

There were other methods of cheating less easily countered. A cunning operator could try to depress one of the scale pans by blowing gently into it, or pick up scraps of gold under a finger nail. On every occasion, of course, both parties to a transaction would wish to check what was being offered with their own set of weights, rather than accepting the other person's word about the exact value of the weights being used.

Adulteration of gold with brass was widespread at times but severely punished. When one senior Ashanti chief was found, after his death, to have adulterated his gold with brass, the king ordered the man's corpse to be dug up and decapitated.

Gold dust, by its very nature, is difficult to handle and easily blown away, dropped or lost. Accidents can happen and "accidents" can be contrived so that one person's gold falls into the receptacle of another. The Ashanti had various ways of keeping their gold dust safe when they were not weighing it out. Quills, plugged at one end, provided handy natural receptacles for the precious material.

Brass boxes were also used, either cast in brass or made out of thin sheet brass, formed by bending and riveting the metal. Even if their lids were very tight-fitting there was still a danger that the finest gold dust would find its way out of them. For this reason the dust was first tied up in tiny scraps of cloth, twisted into little parcels and tied around the neck. A box might contain a number of these bundles.

The *futuo* skin or cloth was also used to prevent cheating or the loss of gold. It was laid out on the ground under the scales so that any gold dust that was dropped would land on top of it and not the ground. Nevertheless, losses undoubtedly occurred, and sometimes these were substantial. According to the law, any gold dropped in the great market at Kumasi belonged to the king and could not be picked up. This law was not only a continuous reminder of royal power but a striking indication of the great volume of daily trading that took place at the centre of the kingdom. Rulers could clearly derive considerable gains from the mistakes and accidental losses of those who had to use gold dust as their daily currency.

BRASS – A RARE COMMODITY

Gold was there for the finding, in many parts of Ashanti it was literally underfoot. On the other hand the brass that was needed for making the weights was far harder to come by. All the brass the Ashanti required had to be imported, and most of it originated thousands of kilometres away in the trading centres of North Africa, Egypt and the Mediterranean world.

It was transported by camel across the Sahara until, transferred to head-loads, it was carried by humans deep into the forest. Some early traders may have brought weights with them but it was the brass vessels they brought that were most eagerly sought by the forest peoples who paid for brass with gold and other commodities. Some of these brass vessels were melted down when they became too damaged to be used, and either local copies or weights were made with the resulting materials. Once the direct sea route from Europe was established by the

This large weight is a mounted warrior clutching a shield and sword, now broken. Horses were rare in the forests, so the warrior portrayed must be from the northern savannah fringes of the Ashanti Empire. It is 11.6 cm (4½ in) high.

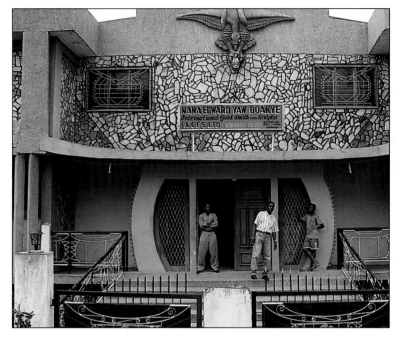

Portuguese at the end of the 15th century, European-made brass began to be imported into the Gold Coast in increasing quantities, not only in the form of brass vessels but also in the form of brass ingots and C-shaped wristlets called *manillas*. European traders quickly realized that there was an exceedingly profitable industry in importing damaged, old-fashioned and second-hand brass. Even brass items that were damaged beyond repair were brought into the Gold Coast.

The brass used to make gold-weights was probably used and then re-used and re-cast as the weights became damaged. Small bits of scrap brass were also pressed into service as weights. It did not matter what they were, as long as they were brass and a suitable weight. A number of items were used in this way: bits of locks, scraps of belt buckles or cap badges, parts of clock mechanisms and even parts of old brass bedsteads. These can still be found in some collections of weights. The manufacture of brass weights must have been the main source of income for many goldsmiths and it is clear that some operated almost a production-line system. In any

One of the most famous and well-respected goldsmiths in the Ashanti region, above left, has the honour of making the Asantehene's gold jewellery. Behind the scenes, skilled craftsmen fashion intricate golden ornaments and jewellery.

large collection of weights one comes across some that are so similar, they must have been made by the same person or by the same team of makers.

The maker, or team of makers, assembled many of these weights from a series of parts, all made to exactly the same shape and size. Many of the depictions of animals or humans in brass-weight form are made up by joining wax rods of different thicknesses; the body made of thick rod, the limbs from thinner rods and so on. It was probably the job of the junior craftsmen to roll out these rods for their masters to work with. We know from more recent observations that apprentices are often similarly employed to cut out wax blanks which are all then decorated by the senior smith who also joins the particular parts together. This probably happened when workshops needed to turn out hundreds of weights each year.

TIMELINE: WORKING WITH GOLD

4000 BC	2000 BC	1000 BC	500 BC	0

Africa

*c.*4000 BC
Egyptians mine placer deposits and open–pit mines between the Nile and the Red Sea.

Tutankhamun was buried in 1323 BC with vast amounts of gold treasure.

*c.*1500 BC
Egyptian tomb paintings show metalsmiths hammering gold objects.

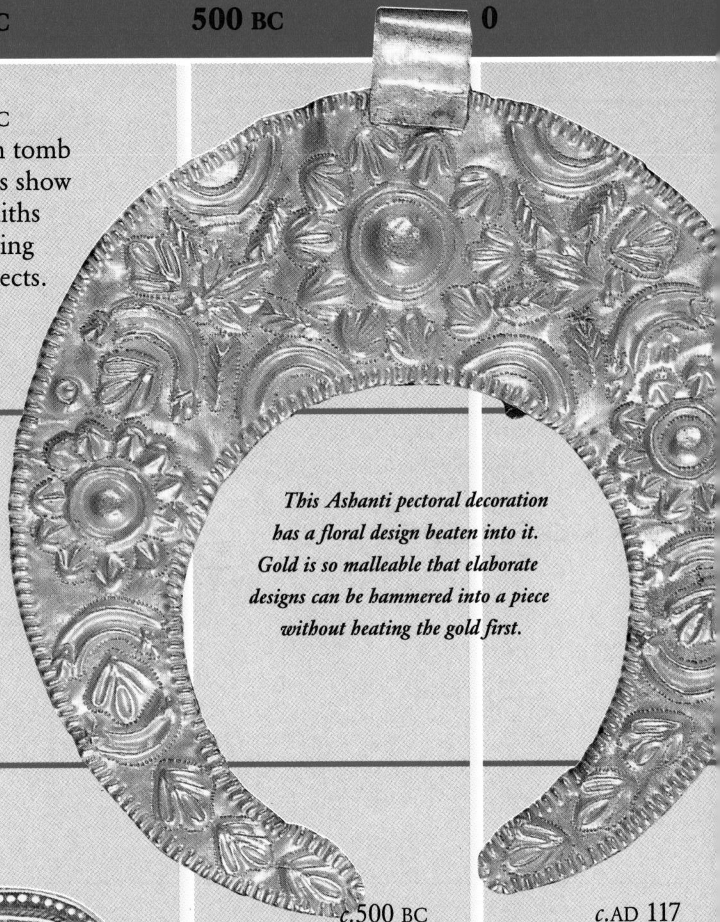

This Ashanti pectoral decoration has a floral design beaten into it. Gold is so malleable that elaborate designs can be hammered into a piece without heating the gold first.

North & South America

*c.*2000 BC
Beaten gold is used at the site of Waywaka in the Andes of southern Peru.

Europe

*c.*3000 BC
Foil gilding starts in Europe.

*c.*2500 BC
Gold lunula found at Orbison, Scotland, dates from this time.

*c.*500 BC
Gold used in dentistry in Rome.

*c.*AD 117
Every gold m[...] known is und[...] the control of the Roman Empire.

*c.*400–250 BC
Etruscans develop the technique of granulation.

This Taplow buckle, dated from the 6th century, is set with garnet. The edge of the buckle, especially the top, features granulation, a technique made famous by the Etruscans.

Australasia

Asia & Middle East

*c.*3000 BC
Gold artefacts dating from this time are buried in a burial tomb at Ur in Sumeria, present-day southern Iraq.

*c.*500–400 BC
Persians mastered the art of chasing, embossing and casting.

*c.*550 BC
Croesus, King of Lydia, mints the first gold coins.

*c.*88 BC
The entire Buddhist canon is written on gold plates.

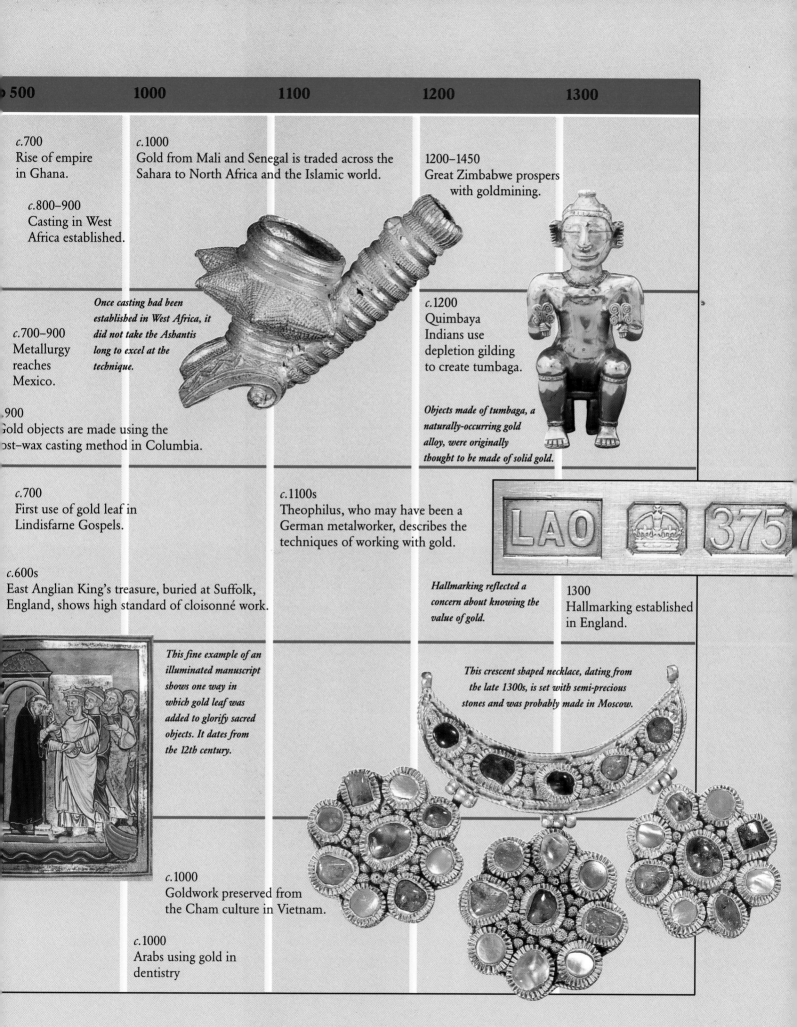

*c.*700
Rise of empire
in Ghana.

*c.*800–900
Casting in West
Africa established.

*c.*1000
Gold from Mali and Senegal is traded across the
Sahara to North Africa and the Islamic world.

1200–1450
Great Zimbabwe prospers
with goldmining.

*Once casting had been
established in West Africa, it
did not take the Ashantis
long to excel at the
technique.*

*c.*700–900
Metallurgy
reaches
Mexico.

*c.*1200
Quimbaya
Indians use
depletion gilding
to create tumbaga.

,900
Gold objects are made using the
ost–wax casting method in Columbia.

*Objects made of tumbaga, a
naturally-occurring gold
alloy, were originally
thought to be made of solid gold.*

*c.*700
First use of gold leaf in
Lindisfarne Gospels.

*c.*1100s
Theophilus, who may have been a
German metalworker, describes the
techniques of working with gold.

*c.*600s
East Anglian King's treasure, buried at Suffolk,
England, shows high standard of cloisonné work.

*Hallmarking reflected a
concern about knowing the
value of gold.*

1300
Hallmarking established
in England.

*This fine example of an
illuminated manuscript
shows one way in
which gold leaf was
added to glorify sacred
objects. It dates from
the 12th century.*

*This crescent shaped necklace, dating from
the late 1300s, is set with semi-precious
stones and was probably made in Moscow.*

*c.*1000
Goldwork preserved from
the Cham culture in Vietnam.

*c.*1000
Arabs using gold in
dentistry

TIMELINE: WORKING WITH GOLD

	1400	1500	1600	1700	1800

Africa

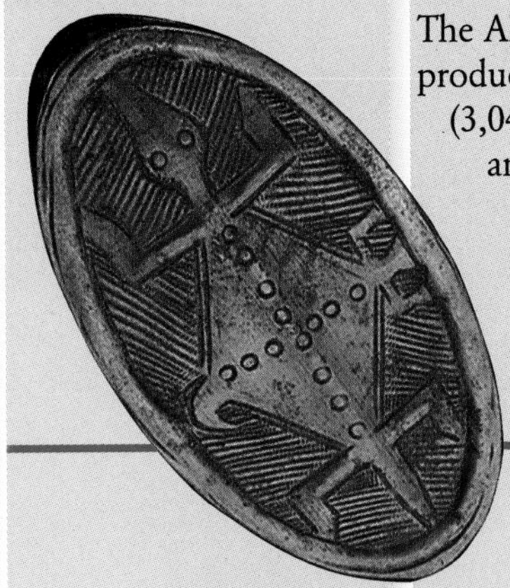

1500
The Akan region produces some 1,380 kg (3,042 lb) of gold annually.

1600
Gold dust is used as currency in Ghana.

1500–1800
Ghanaian gold trade with Europe.

When gold dust was used as currency in Ghana, the valuable dust was kept in small parcels in decorative brass boxes.

This Ashanti sword handle is based on a European design.

North & South America

c.1400–1500
The Inca in Peru crafted figurines with multicomponent sheet construction and soldered joints.

1523
When the Spanish arrive in the New World, they find that the Inca have already learned the art of beating, annealing, embossing and chasing.

1848
California gold rush.

Europe

c.1500–71
Benvenuto Cellini, Italian goldsmith, produces exquisite goldwork, but only one of his pieces survives today.

1769
The Watt steam engine patented.

1789
The French Revolution.

1814
Castellani set up his workshop in Rome.

This turban ornament features both gold and enamelled decoration. Gold thread was a popular form of gold decoration in Asia.

This Chinese chair covering, dated c.1700s, features the Qilin, *a creature of good omen.*

Australasia

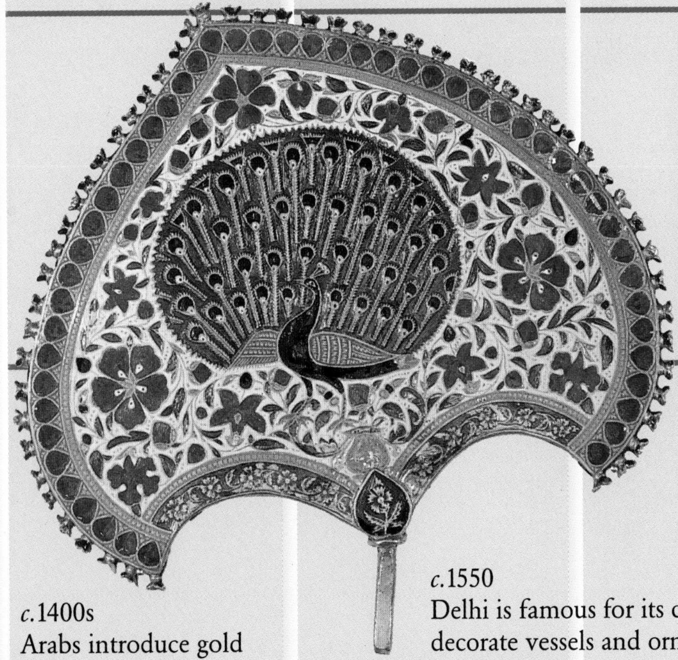

1851
Australian gold rush.

1861
Gold found in New Zealand.

Asia & Middle East

c.1400s
Arabs introduce gold tooling to Europe.

c.1550
Delhi is famous for its craftsmen that decorate vessels and ornaments of jade with gold inlay.

c.1700s
The Chinese use gold thread to embroider cloth.

1744
Gold discovered in the Urals, Russia.

1887
The MacArthur-Forrest cyanide
process for extracting gold
introduced in South Africa.

1886
Gold rush in
South Africa.

1896
Alaskan gold rush.

1930s
Fort Knox built.

1967
South Africa produces
first Krugerrand.
This one-ounce bullion
coin becomes a favourite
of individual investors
around the world

1965
Gold used in the helmet
visor in the first space walk,
18 March 1965.

*Gold was used in the space helmet in the first
space walk. Gold is an unreactive metal and thus
has many technological uses.*

66
namite invented
Alfred Nobel.

1927
Gold used in the
treatment for
rheumatoid arthritis.

1980
Brazil's gold rush.

*Much of modern Ashanti
jewellery is cast using
traditional methods.*

1975
Factories use machines to mass produce
jewellery while a few artist-craftsmen maintain
their artistically significant work.

*The invention of dynamite and its
application in gold mining meant that
more ore could be removed for processing,
resulting in more gold in circulation.*

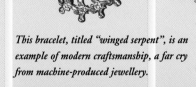

*This Chinese-style winter landscape pendant,
by Rene Jules, was made in Paris in 1900.
The small pine cones are cast gold.*

*This bracelet, titled "winged serpent", is an
example of modern craftsmanship, a far cry
from machine-produced jewellery.*

*Gold has a wealth of uses
throughout Asia and it forms
the basis of much trade today.*

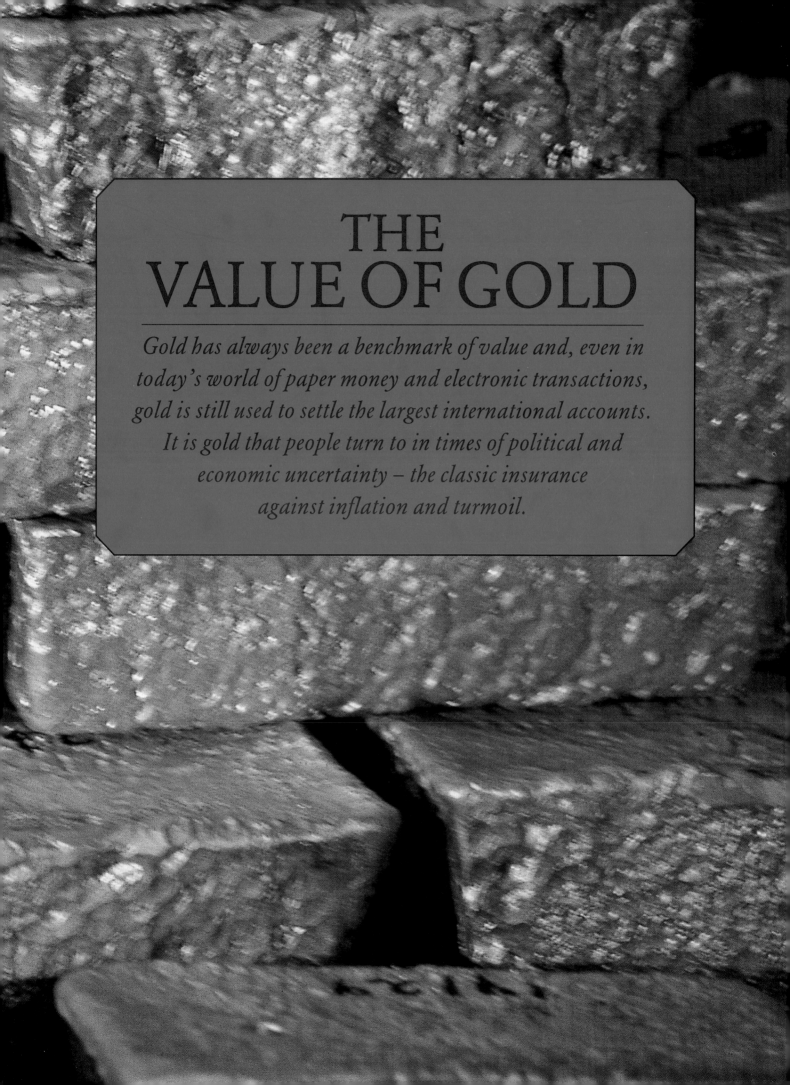

THE VALUE OF GOLD

Gold has always been a benchmark of value and, even in today's world of paper money and electronic transactions, gold is still used to settle the largest international accounts. It is gold that people turn to in times of political and economic uncertainty – the classic insurance against inflation and turmoil.

THE VALUE OF GOLD

"You have to choose between trusting the natural stability of gold and the natural stability of the honesty and intelligence of the members of the Government and, with due respect to these gentlemen, I advise you to vote for gold." (George Bernard Shaw)

Since the beginning of recorded history gold has invited comparison with all that is pure, noble, virtuous, elegant, charismatic, precious and authentic. Gold is the first metal to be mentioned in the Bible (Genesis 2:10–12), and people's psychological attachment to it was – and is still – so strong that on the only occasion in the Old Testament that the Jews turned away from worshipping God, they turned to a golden calf. The Greek myth of Jason and the Argonauts' search for the golden fleece has triggered the literary imagination of generations, and King Midas, who wished that everything he touched turned to gold, has come to represent the ultimate in human greed.

From the days of Classical antiquity, gold has symbolized people's desires and achievements – all that they held most precious. And this symbolic role was particularly evident in the fields of religion and politics, where the use of gold in the accoutrements of office, in statues, medals, and so on reflected the spiritual and aesthetic aspirations of a society as well as more material values. As the French philosopher Boileau noted: "Even unto ugliness a little gold lends a touch of beauty." Nowadays, we automatically think of gold as one of the most valuable substances on earth. Weight for weight, it is far more precious than virtually all other metals and we can easily find

Ashanti gold is transported by air to Switzerland, the international capital for money transactions and gold trade. There it is refined and turned into bars and ingots, or bullion.

out, at any time of the day or night, how many dollars, pounds, francs or cedis an ounce of gold is worth. In times of crisis many people would prefer to have assets in the form of gold rather than in paper money or property: because gold is universally accepted as an item of enduring value, divorced from the fluctuations of national currencies. The underlying assumption is that everyone will want gold if they can get it.

Yet it has not always been like this – many societies have had little use for the metal, and there have been some which have put a far higher value on other things or have even ignored gold completely. The people of ancient Ghana, for example, were more than ready to exchange large quantities of gold for items they valued more, such as salt, iron, brass and copper. The original inhabitants of Australia had no use for gold, even though gold nuggets could be found in their territories, and the trading system used by Papua New Guineans placed a very high value on items such as pigs, pearl shells, stone axes and even Bird of Paradise feathers.

When Columbus first reached the Americas the natives of Hispaniola (modern-day Haiti and the Dominican Republic) must, from his own account, have found his interest in gold puzzling. They used it to make necklaces, nose rings and other items of adornment but his passionate interest in the metal was primarily as money. Columbus was not interested in the forms of the gold objects he acquired, only in their purchasing power once he returned to Europe. The Spanish conquistadors who

followed Columbus showed the same clash of values when they reached the gold-producing areas of the New World: they took sacred gold objects and melted them down to turn them into anonymous gold bars to be shipped back to the royal mints of Spain. For the Inca of Peru, gold was intimately connected with the gods and worship; for the Spanish, it was something to be made into coins, to gain economic and political dominance over the rest of the world.

The Ashanti society is an example of how gold is valued, along with food and drink, as an indication of happiness and prosperity. The Kings of Ashanti recognized a duty to provide gold dust for important and influential strangers who visited the capital; they even did this for Europeans being held prisoner there. The amounts distributed in this way were considerable, especially as they were nearly always combined with the gift of food and drink. One visitor, who was at Kumasi in 1816, received a cow, two pigs, 15 sheep, 331 yams, 671 bunches of plantain and more than 20 oz of gold dust. There was a formal quality about this gold-giving but its desired effect was clearly stated by the Asantehene Osei Bonsu: "I must give them gold and provisions and send them home happy and rich, that it may be known in other countries that I am a great king, and know what is right."

Gold as currency

We can trace the way gold began to take on a role in the exchange of diverse goods, and how it began to be used as money throughout societies around the world. Records from Mesopotamia, dating from around 2400 BC, show that silver was being weighed out for payment of land rents, compensation and taxes. By 2000 BC silver was also being used to make purchases and to pay wages. Once this principle had been established it was only a matter of time before gold was put to the same use. Egyptian tomb paintings from 1400 BC show gold rings being weighed out as tribute. Sometimes a character in the shape of a ring was used to signify the name of a unit of weight, which strongly suggests that a form of gold ring currency was evolving.

Similar systems have, of course, survived until very recently. The Ashanti used gold dust as their currency until 1901 and in Madagascar, in the 19th century, imported silver coins were melted down and cast into bars so they could be used by weight. In China, until the early decades of the 20th century, silver was also used by weight in carrying out commercial transactions. Other societies in the past have used cocoa beans and slabs of copper and even stone discs as currency.

Whatever the currency used for trade, whether it is shells, beans, brass or feathers, it is best if the chosen material is both durable and easily divisible into units of different sizes. It must also be fairly portable and hard to counterfeit. It is obvious that gold, once it has been hardened by alloying it with another metal, is splendidly suited to serve as money, especially as it is never consumed, although it may change its form over time.

It was the great invention of the Lydians in the late 7th century BC that helped simplify and extend the role of gold and silver as money: they produced standardized weights of precious metal and stamped them to guarantee their value – they created coins. Once coins had been invented, gold and silver were increasingly used to compare and calculate the values of a vast range of things, including people, animals, weapons and food. However, to function effectively as money any type of material will have to be tied into a wider system of measurement: there must be ways of counting, measuring and weighing it. An exchange system using money cannot operate

very well if the counting system runs out at six or seven or if there is no way of deciding if one sack of flour weighs more than another.

THE IMPORTANCE OF WRITING

There is another element that can make a money system more flexible: writing. Once transactions can be written down, the way is open to carrying them out, not by the exchange of coins or gold bars for goods, but by noting down on paper who owes what to whom. When writing is used, money need not change hands immediately. All that is needed is a regular settling up of what is owed at the end of an agreed period of time.

There have, of course, been many societies where the movement of money was recorded without recourse to writing. The Ashanti were one of these. For everyday transactions at the royal court, a group of officials was responsible for weighing in or out the

sums of gold dust that were needed. Withdrawals were recorded by placing a cowrie shell for every peredwan unit (about 70 g/2$^{1}/_{2}$ oz) of gold dust removed. Once a system of payment involving writing has been established, it is not such a long step to the type of transactions we have today, where money is transferred in and out of accounts in the form of electronic impulses.

CREATING A GOLD STANDARD

The great flow of gold from Africa and the Americas after the 15th century helped fuel the economic growth and expansion of Europe. Despite wars and disputes, by the start of the 18th century Great Britain was beginning to emerge as a major economic

Gold dust was carried in brass boxes, like the one opposite, when gold was used as currency in Ashanti. Today, much of their gold is stored in Switzerland as gold bars, below.

force. In 1717, the British mint, under the direction of Sir Isaac Newton, established a fixed price for an ounce of gold. On this certainty a massive economic system was about to develop.

Although silver continued to circulate in Great Britain, from that time onwards the standard value of gold served as the basis of the growing British economy. The basic rule was that silver and bank notes could be freely exchanged for gold and people could have their bullion turned into coins or coins into bullion. The most important point was that everyone knew the exact value of gold and had confidence that they could exchange their money for gold whenever they wanted for whatever they wanted.

DEVELOPING A SYSTEM

About this time many other nations discovered that they could issue paper money if it was supported by and exchangeable for gold. Some countries, discovering that not everyone who had accepted paper currency wanted to change it back into gold at the same time, began to print far more money than they had gold. The inflation that inevitably resulted was followed by a collapse of confidence and a run on banks.

The American colonies, for example, were forbidden by King George III of Great Britain to print paper money, but the Continental Congress did so anyway. Because they lacked the gold to support their paper currency, inflation increased dramatically. The complete collapse of the fledgling economy was only averted by France, Spain and the Netherlands making large loans of gold and silver. By contrast, the Bank of England and British commercial banks took great care that any paper money they issued was well supported by actual gold.

The gold doré bars that leave the Ashanti Goldfields Company are not all the same weight. They have to be refined down to these smooth bars, all of which will have an exact weight.

A cargo of gold is weighed at the Ashanti Goldfields Company before being boxed for transportation to the refinery in Switzerland, where it will also be stored.

In 1818 the British government formally placed its economy on the gold standard. The system, which was in time accepted by most major and many secondary powers, had a number of key elements. The main ones were that gold had a fixed price in relation to other currencies and that bullion and coins could be freely interchanged. All other monies, whether coins of different metals or bank notes, could be turned into gold at the fixed price without restriction, and gold could be turned into them at the same price. Gold could also be used to make purchases between nations and to settle any international debts without restrictions on its movement in and out of countries. It was this general freedom of movement of gold and the free convertibility of other monies into gold at a fixed rate that lay at the heart of the system. Of course, people might prefer paper money for all sorts of reasons, not least of all for the convenience.

In the 19th century, most banks and governments were extremely careful to maintain a high ratio of gold to the number of notes in circulation. Towards the end of the 19th century, for example, the United States kept reserves of about 25 percent against notes and deposits, Italy kept no less than 60 percent. Great Britain, however, relying on the highly respected reputation of its currency, was able to keep reserves of only around 3.5 percent.

A WORLDWIDE STANDARD

In the mid-19th century, with the California and Australia gold rushes, there was a huge leap in the amount of gold that entered circulation as coin. Prior to this time, the average annual value of gold coins minted by Great Britain, France and the United States was $8.4 million; by 1851 it had risen to $75 million. The world supply of gold doubled between 1850 and 1875 and, even more impressively, in the 12 years between 1850 and 1862 the monetary supply of gold doubled. This vast rise in the amount

Ghanaian currency is based on the cedi. Until 1901, gold dust was used as money. Paper money is just as small and portable as gold dust, but perhaps a little more practical.

of gold available for use as money was one of the factors that brought an increasing number of nations on to the gold standard in the closing decades of the 19th century and in the early years of the 20th century, especially after the gold discoveries in South Africa. By 1900, nearly 30 nations were on the gold standard, and the figure increased to almost 60 by 1914. The pre-1914 gold standard system provided the foundation of a single worldwide currency system.

Using the gold standard had many advantages, and even today some economists and bankers look at these with longing. The most obvious one was that

trade and economic activity were not subject to government rules and regulations: imports and exports could flow freely provided there was money available to pay for them. Anyone who had access to gold or could prove that their money was securely backed by gold, could buy and sell as they wished. Secondly, currencies were stable: everyone knew the worth of any currency and there was no fear of the sudden changes in the value of the dollar or the franc that the world has since experienced with more recent floating-exchange systems. Thirdly, national governments had little chance to try to manage the economy of their states, which appeals to those who blame government economic policies for the post-1945 booms and slumps in the economy.

In theory, under the gold standard, economic activity was controlled automatically without government intervention: when a country found itself spending more than it earned its gold would flow out. This meant that there was less money in circulation, which would reduce demand, bring down prices and make its exports cheaper and more attractive, thereby inducing gold to flow back in to that country.

The outflow of gold leading to a diminution of prices and an increase in the cost of borrowing affected even such groups as the Ashanti. By the 18th century they had become inextricably enmeshed in the international trade system as key providers of gold to the state mints and the bankers and businessmen of Europe. Gold was flowing out of their own economy and they took imported goods in exchange: guns, rum, gin, cloth, silver, metalware, and so on. As a result, during the 19th century, there seems to have been a shortage of gold in Ashanti. This was caused in part by the abolition of the slave trade in the 1820s, which meant that virtually all

imports had to be paid for in gold. This shortage of gold within the Ashanti economy was reflected in the high rates of interest on loans. Under King Osei Tutu Kwame (1804–23), for example, the rate of 33 percent for a 42-day period (the basic period within the Ashanti calendar) was recorded.

THE GOLD STANDARD AND WORLD WARS

The system of international trade and stable gold prices ended with the outbreak of the First World War. Gold could not be allowed to be traded between fighting nations, especially as many of them began printing money without the backing of gold bullion. The free flow of trade ended and countries began to withdraw gold coins from circulation and to forbid their citizens to hold gold bullion or coins. They then set about trying to manage their economies.

After peace in 1918, attempts were made to revive the gold standard in a modified form and by 1931 there were 50 nations involved in the new system. The details varied: some countries, such as France and Great Britain, had a bullion standard, which meant that money could be changed into gold bars but not coins, while others adhered to the traditional coin system. However, the incompatibility between the rates of their own currency and the rates for gold set by different countries – along with the economic policies by which they tried to manage their economies while still operating within the gold standard – led to its collapse in the early 1930s.

THE INTERNATIONAL MONETARY FUND

By 1932, for example, many citizens of the United States tried to convert their assets into gold, creating a number of runs on the banks. As a result, the United States abandoned the gold standard and set about ensuring that its citizens turned in all the gold they possessed by making it illegal to hold the metal. Eventually, Fort Knox was built, with its enormously thick concrete and steel vaults, to store all the gold

The changing value of gold

For 1 oz of gold you could:

1997
buy 6 top-price tickets at a London theatre

buy 6 dozen oysters

buy 8 bottles of champagne

1800s
pay school fees at Eton for half a term

hire a farm labourer for 7 weeks

buy 25 dozen oysters

1600s
hire a weaver, cloth-worker or dyer for 1 year and 8 months

buy 340 g (12 oz) tea

buy 78 kg (172 lb) tobacco

1400s
buy 25 kg (54 lb) of sealing wax

buy 18 litres (4 gallons) of wine

Pay a candle maker for 64 days

buy 13 reams of paper

1200s
pay 6 wolf catchers to work for one year

pay a horn blower in the king's court for 76 days

pay a groom for 1 year and 4 months

rent 134 market stalls for a year

the government removed from circulation. In 1934, the government raised the price of gold to $35 an ounce and decreed that henceforth it would only redeem its liabilities in gold to foreign central banks and treasuries, the "qualified gold bullion standard". The free convertibility on which the gold standard depended was gone.

But other treasuries and central banks were allowed access to the United States' great stockpile of gold. An agreement in 1944 set up the International Monetary Fund, giving both gold and dollars a central role as key currencies in international government financing. In the next two decades, the United States found that as other nations became increasingly prosperous and held more dollars, its gold reserves were becoming smaller and smaller as those nations exercised their right to convert the dollars into gold. Eventually, in the 1970s, the United States was forced to devalue gold from its fixed value and to end its commitment to give out gold in exchange for dollars.

ELECTRONIC FUNDS

In today's age of "high-tech wizardry" it is not unimaginable or indeed unusual for "money" to be transferred in and out of accounts in the form of electronic impulses, with no physical type of transaction taking place whatsoever. Further, with the onset of telephone banking, people can make monetary transactions without actually leaving their homes and going to the bank. And, once people have got used to treating little bits of paper or electronic messages as if they represent something real and tangible, then there seems to be no need for money to be supported by gold at all. The only problem then becomes: who controls the amount of credit that people can have and who decides on the number of notes in circulation. Electronic buying,

selling and banking is a long way from the earlier use of gold bars or coins as money for trade. The history of gold over the last 200 years or so is, to a considerable degree, a story of its early predominance in the world's monetary system, and then its gradual elimination, which is something that many find disturbing, with all its futuristic possibilities, and that, from time to time, seems due to be reversed.

GOLD AS MONEY TODAY

Gold holdings constitute a substantial portion of the reserve assets of central banks throughout the world. In 1985, for example, the world's central banks and government-controlled investment institutions were the net purchasers of an estimated 135 tonnes of gold. Many of the gold-producing countries of Asia, Africa and Latin America also boost their own reserves by purchasing local mine output rather than immediately selling it on the market in order to raise foreign exchange.

Gold is also used as collateral by central banks to secure loan facilities from other such banks. A classic example of this occurred in the 1970s when the Italian central bank, faced with extreme difficulties with funding the deficit in its foreign trade accounts, pledged part of its gold reserves at market prices in order to obtain a loan from the then West German Bundesbank. The dramatic improvement in Italy's external accounts in subsequent years enabled its central bank not only to repay the West German central bank but also to resume full ownership of its gold reserves.

Central banks and treasuries pay off debts to one another by moving gold. Many countries hold major reserves in centres such as New York and transfers are effected simply by moving gold bars from one identified locker to another.

SWAPPING MONEY

Gold swapping is brought into play when gold prices are low and it is not prudent to dispose of stock. In these circumstances, a central bank may deposit its gold with a leading commercial bank in Europe or North America at an agreed rate of exchange for short-term loan facilities.

A classic example of this took place in 1976 when the South African Reserve Bank, facing its worst-ever balance of payments situation, concluded a swap arrangement with the three biggest Swiss commercial banks, receiving under the agreement a substantial foreign exchange facility. At the time of the agreement the average price of gold was US$150 per ounce. By 1979, when repayment was due, the unit price of gold had risen dramatically and the South African Reserve Bank found itself in the position of repaying its swap facility by selling its gold at well over US$500 per ounce.

GOLD'S STRATEGIC INVESTORS

By buying shares in quoted gold-mining companies, investors receive dividends as well as benefiting from increases in the share price. Another avenue open to strategic investors is the gold options market: an option is the right to buy or sell a specific quantity of gold. Options usually offer potential for profit but where losses occur they are limited to the initial investment.

In the gold futures market, commitments are made to buy or sell designated amounts of gold at a specific time in the future at an agreed price. None of these contracts entails the physical handling of gold, unlike hedging which involves trading in gold or gold artefacts by entering into the futures market.

Real gold, curiously enough, is still used in settling international debts. When central banks and government treasuries come to pay off their debts to each other they do so with real gold, by "remote control". They hold major reserves in places like New York and in order to effect a transfer, the correct number of gold bars are trundled from their locker on one side of an underground strong room to the recipient's locker on the other side. Thus the precious metal wrested from beneath the earth in distant lands finds another subterranean resting place, beneath a major city's busy streets.

INVESTING IN GOLD

Gold has two distinct advantages: it cannot be inflated by the printing of more paper money, nor can governments devalue it. The private purchase of gold coins, for example, is attractive because although these coins do not pay dividends, their unit price tends to rise in terms of the money used to purchase them.

South African Krugerrands were popular until the political realities of South Africa discouraged people from buying them. The United States minted commemorative coins in 1984 to mark the Olympic Games, and still enjoys sales of its 1986 gold coin, the Eagle, made from newly minted American gold. Other countries, including Ghana, issue commemorative coins to celebrate important events as well as for private investors who may simply want to hoard gold for the future.

Numismatics is the collection or study of gold coins, which are valued because of their near-perfect condition and rarity. In this case, a gold coin is as desirable and collectable as any other work of fine art, and one that will last for more than one lifetime.

The Ashanti Goldfields Company was listed on the New York Stock Exchange in 1996, making history by being the first African operating company to appear there.

INDEX

Note: numbers in *italic* refer to maps, boxes or plans

A

Accra 17, 18, 24
Acheampong, Col Ignatius 18
acid, for leaching 144-5
Adansi 10, 11, 12
Adinkra symbols *154*
adits 10, 12, 14, 70
    see also mining: shallow
adulteration 173-6
Africa 9, *13*, 22
    AGC and 9, 10, 12, 22
        first New York listing 24, 195
    "jungle boom" 17
    North 124-5, 126, 176
    political boundaries 130
    slaves in S. America 104, 129
    smuggling 130-2, *131*
    Tiny Rowland and 23
    West 36, *131*
        European trade, early 125-8, 126-7
        gold boom 49
        Islam and 124-5
        panning 55
        prospecting, modern 49
    see also South Africa
agate, for polishing 143
AGC *see* Ashanti Goldfields Company
Agogo area 157-8
aircraft 41
Akan peoples 68, 72, 111, 125-8, 149, *154*
    see also Ashanti
Akoben people 145
Akosombo Dam 20
Alexander III the Great, king of Macedon 35, 123
alloys 37, 38, 41
    adulteration 173
    amalgams 11, 62, 144
    ancient 137
    and colour 35, 39, *39*
    created 39, 144
        for currency 186
        for extraction 62-3
        solders 138
    and gilding 144-5
    natural 35, 39, 123, 152
    see also copper
alluvial gold *see* placer
amalgams 11, 62, 144
Amazon region 48
Amegashie, R. Sylvan 18, 19
AMEP (Ashanti Mines Expansion Programme) 21-4
America, North 46-8, 55, 105-8
    metal-working 144
    paper money 188
    see also United States; Canada
America, South/Central 112, 187
    Columbus 125, 185-6
    metal-working 144-6, 146
    Portuguese and 103, 104-6
    Spanish and 35-6, 42-4, 53, 103-4, 144, 185-6
    Spanish treasure-ships 128-9, 128-9, *131*
    see also specific places
Amritsar, India 124
Angola 22
Ankobra river 10, 45
Ankrah, General 18, 19
annealing 138

Anokye, Komfo 150, 170
anti-missile reflectors 41
Anyemaim *15*
Anyinam mine 75
Appiah, Peggy 172
archaeology
    and grave-robbing 48
Archimedean screw 102-3, *102*
Arctic regions 55
    see also Klondike
Argonauts 185
    "forty-niners" 45
arsenic 23
Asantehemaa (Queen Mother) 153
Asantehenes (kings) 66, 128, 139, 143, 148, 150-1, 152-8, 157, 168, 169, 171, 177
    Golden Stool 66, 150-1, *150*, 157
    oath swords 152, 157, 170
Ashanti 111, 125-6
    artefacts 139, 140, 143-5, 149-77
        hallmarks 147
        helmets 28, 161
        jewellery 36, 128, 132, 136, 147
        ritual/ceremonial 28, 122, 139, 145, 148, 149, 150-8, 167
    burial systems 29
    calendar 190
    court criers 140, 156, 164
    currency, *see under* gold dust
    empire of 9, 10, 11, 65-6, 111, 126
        accounting 187
        dismantled by British 12, 66, 170
        gold culture 29, 168-71, 186
        Golden Stool 66, 150-1, *150*, 157
        goldsmiths, imported 168-70
        slavery 16-17, 111-12, 126, 128, 170, 190
        status-rules 170-2
    gold-mining 9, 10, 64, 65-73, 111-12, 126, 170, 172, *172*, 174-6, 176-7, 188
        deep mining 72-3
        European methods 10-11, 12, 65-6
        miners 101, 111-12
        modern *see* mining
        origins 65
        rights/remuneration 71
        smuggling 131-2, *131map*
        techniques used 65, 66, 68-73, 69-70, 101-2
        weights *see* weights
    goldsmiths 167-70, 171-2, 177, *177*
    "red gold" 29
    religion 122, 126, 170
    sike ne obene 150
    spokesmen/linguists 143, 155-6, 159
    trade 65, 69, 123, 125-8, 171-7, 190
        gold dust currency 29, 123, 186, 187
        gold shortage, 19 cent. 190
        gold unvalued 185
    see also Ghana; Gold Coast
Ashanti Goldfields Company (AGC) 8-25
    community interests 20, 116-19
    early mining 10-18, 71, 73-4, 104-5, 108-9
        labour shortages 15, 16
        lodes mined 74
        panorama 18-19
        personnel 110-11
    government receipts 16, 17, 18
        AGC capital supported 19
    headquarters at Obuasi 68, 100

history 10-25
    Cade era 11-14, *17*
    "Company" established 68
    "Company" re-established 18
    Corporation founded 10, 12, 47, 65, 68
    decline, post-WWII 17-18
    head office in Accra 18, 24
    Lonrho acquires 18, 18-19, 23
    pan-African interests 9, 22, 25
    renaissance, 1980s 19-21
    stock exchange listings 18, 24, 24, 195
    museum 116
    output figures
        early 10, 12, 16, 18-19, 74
        modern 19, 21
        timber concessions 20
        see also Obuasi; mine-workers
Ashanti lode/mine 15, 16, 74
    see also Obuasi
Ashanti Mines Expansion Programme (AMEP) 21-4
assaying 80-1
astronauts 40, 41
astronomy 41
"Atenteben" 118
Atumtufuo 156
Au symbol 30
Australia 9, 15, 31, 42, 185
    gold-rush 46, 109, 189
    "largest nugget in the world" 42
avoirdupois weight 38-9
Awuda 10
Ayanfuri mine 9, 22, 88-9
Ayenim mine 15
Azambuja, Diego d' 125
Aztec people 42

B

bacteria treatment 23-4, 90-3, *90*
beating/hammering 33-4, *33*, 137, 138, 141-3
Bekwai 10, 11, 12
bellows 137, 145, 168
benches *78*
Benin 126
Bibiani mine 9, 22
Biney, Chief Joseph Edward ("Tarkwa") 9, 10-11, 12, *13*, *15*, 68
Biox plant/bio-leaching 23-4, 90-3
Birim river 56
bismuth oxide 41
Blackee's ventilation shaft 78-9
"blanket", corduroy 55, 62
blasting 11, 12, 13, 78, 84, 88
boats, heated glass 41
Boer War 12, 13
boilers 20, 112-13
Bomburi 22
Bonanza (Rabbit Creek) 47
Bonnat, Marie-Joseph 10, 66-7, 172
books, and gold leaf 34, 35, 143-4
Botchwey, Dr Kwesi 19
Bowditch, Thomas 149
brass 166, 168, 176-7
    alloyed with gold, adulteration 173-6
    Ashanti value 176, 185
    gold-boxes 172, 172-3, 176, 187
    lamps 162
    vessels 125, 126, 170, 176-7
    weights 158, 170, 172, 176-7
Brazil 104-6
    gold-rush 48, *48*, 104-6

Britain
    AGC and 9
    gold and economy 187-8
    gold reserves 189
    gold standard 188-9
        bullion standard 190
    Goldsmiths, Company of 147
    guineas 123
    hallmarking 146-7
    nobles (coins) 124
    Spanish gold 36, 44
    W. African gold 9, 10, 36, 65, 125
        Gold Coast (Ghana) colonized 11, 12, *15*, 65-6, 170
bronze 123, 130, 138, 144, 168
Brown, Joseph P. 9, 10-11, *11*, 12
building technology, gold and 41
bullion/ingots
    bullion standard 190-2
    and currency 188, 189
    see also ingots
Burkina Faso 22
Burma, Golden Rock 141
Busia, Dr K.A. 18, 156

C

Cade, Edwin 9, 11-14, 14, *17*, 68, 73
calaverite 31
California 56
    gold-rush 31, 45-6, 107-8, 189
    panning elaborated 55, 56
Canada 9
    Klondike gold-rush 46-8
cap, ceremonial 140
Cape Coast [Castle] 10, 11, 12, 13, *13*, 14, *17*, 125
capitalism 125
carbon-in-leach treatment 89
cars, heated glass 34, 41
Cartagena, Colombia 44
cased/rolled gold 146
casting 140, 158-67
    early 32
    hollow 164-5
    lost-beetle 162-4
    lost-wax (*cire-perdue*) 140, 144, 150-1, 160-4, 173-5
    precision work 166-7, 169
    red earth technique 167
charcoal, and casting 164, 166
chemicals 20, 88
    see also specific chemicals
chiefs 145, 152-65
Chilkoot Pass 47
China 34, 186
Christianborg Castle 125
cire-perdue see casting: lost-wax
claim-staking 48, 108
clay, and casting 164-5, 166
cloth of gold 34-5
Cluff Resources company 22
cocoa 128, 132, 186
coins 35-7, 123-4, 185-95
    clipped 37
    commemorative 38, 194
    die-stamping 36
    early 35, 186
    as investment 194
    numismatics 194
    prestige 123, 124
    proliferation 189
    thinned 37
cold-working, of gold 152-8
Colombia 138, 146
    treasure fleets 44, 128

Colorado 31, 32
Columbus, Christopher 35, 42, 125, 185
computers 41
Congo, Democratic Republic of 22
Constantine I the Great, Emperor 123
copper 185
    alloyed with gold 31, 35, 37, 39, 142
        adulteration 173
        as granule-solder 140
        removal of 62
        tumbaga 144-5
    bronze 123, 130, 138, 144, 168
    as currency 186
    found with gold 32
    hammered 33
    melting-point 32, 145
    oxide/oxidization 32, 144-5
    smelting 32, 168
corduroy "blanket" 55, 62
core-samples 77, 80-1
Cortés, Hernán 42
Côte d'Ivoire 22, 131, 154
Côte d'Or lode 70, 74, 86
Côte d'Or Mining Company 11-12, 14
cradle see rocker
Croesus, king of Lydia 123
cross-cuts 58
crown 138
crushing 15, 16, 21, 63, 88
    stamp mills 11, 15, 105-6
crystals 30, 31, 32, 53
    weathering 54
cupels 80
currency
    gold as 29, 123-4, 186-95
        accounting 186-7
        gold dust 171-6; see also under gold dust
        investment 194
        national holdings 192-4
        numismatics 194
        purchasing values 191
        stability 189-90
        swapping 194
    inflation 188-9
        electronic transfer 187, 192
    paper money 181, 187-92
    writing and 187
    see also coins
Cuzco, Peru, Temple of the Sun 43
cyanide 15, 62-3, 90

D

Daw, John 12, 13, 14, 43, 73
deforestation 90, 92
    reforestation 16, 63, 95
Denkyira 170
dentistry 41
diamond drills 60
diamonds, weight in karats 38
die-stamping 36
digging-sticks 70
dinar 124
Dominassi 17
doré bars 77, 96-7, 188
Drake, Sir Francis 44
draw-plates 138
drawing, of gold 33, 34-5
dredging 56-7, 109
    Ghana 56-7, 56

drills 59, 60, 78-9, 81, 83, 86
    compressed-air 61
    diamond 60
    sampling 81
drives 58
Dubai 132, 133
ducats 124
dynamite 59-60, 84

E

Eagles (coins) 194
Eburahene 171
economics 185-95
Ecuador 145
Edward II, king of England 147
Egypt 126, 176
    Ancient 123
        gold and burial systems 29, 31
        gold crafts 34, 137, 141
        gold as currency 186
        Tutankhamen 30, 31, 34, 141
        Archimedean screw 102-3
        and Mali gold 124
Ekaterinburg, Russia 106
electrical engineering 34, 41
electricity supplies
    for community 119
    mining applications 20, 59-61
electrum 35, 123, 130
Elizabeth I, queen of England 36
Ellis, Joseph Ettruson 9, 10-11, 12, 13, 15, 68
Ellis mine 10-11, 13
Ellis shaft 10
Elmina 125, 126-7
environmental concerns 23-4, 90-7, 117
    air sampling 95, 97
    waste minimalization 94
Eritrea 22
Escobar, Pedro de 125
Essamen mine 45
Ethiopia 22
Etruscans 138-40
Europe
    brass 176-7
    Ghana, artistic traces 148, 156, 171
    gold coins minted 124-5
    gold and economies 187-8
    W. African trade 124-8, 149, 186
explosives 20, 59-60, 62, 84, 88
    gunpowder 11, 13, 59

F

famfa 173, 176
Fante people 10
Ferdinand II, king of Spain 53
filigree 137
filler plant 105
fire gilding 144
flooding 59, 102-3
florins 124
flotation treatment 89
fluxes 63
foil 34, 152
France 10
    bullion standard 190
    gold coins 124
    piracy 44
Francis II, king of France 39
Freda Rebecca mine, Zimbabwe 9, 22
Frederick II, Emperor 124
furnaces 168
fusing 33
futuo 172-3, 176

G

galamsey 10, 90-2
Gaulle, Gen. Charles de 21
George III, king of England 188
George Cappendell Shaft 20, 57, 78-9
Germany, Bundesbank 192
Ghana 9, 22, 67, 131
    British colonize see under Gold Coast
    cocoa 16
    currency 189, 194
    Economic Recovery Programme (1980s) 19
    geology/minerals 66-7
    gold 9, 10, 10-25, 64, 65-73, 112-19
        economic benefits 9, 10, 16, 17, 18, 117
        government's controlling interest 18, 24
        Minerals and Mining legislation (1986) 9, 19
        output 19, 21
        regulation 117
    Mine Workers' Union 115
    National Liberation Council 17-18, 19
    Parliament 154-5
    Presidency 154
    Provisional National Defence Council 20
    Republic established 9, 38, 154
        military régimes 17-19
    Trade Union Congress 25
    see otherwise Gold Coast; Ashanti and specific topics
gilding 142, 143-6
    depletion gilding 144-5, 146
glass, gold and 34, 40, 41
gold 26-49, 178-81
    artefacts 33-5, 137-77
        ancient 129-30, 137, 138-41
        Ashanti 149-77
        joining techniques 137-8
        see also wire; beating; leaf
    chemical symbol 30
    colour of 39, 39
        and glass manufacture 41
        greenish 34, 39
        and purity tests 37, 38
        red 29, 31, 39, 167
        sika kokoo (red gold) 29
        silver content and 35, 39
        white 39
    compounds 31-2
    crystals 30, 31, 32, 53, 54
    currency see currency
    early exploitation 30, 31, 53
        coinage 35
        drawing 34
        flood prevention 59, 102-3
        melting 32
    exploration 48-9, 80
    extraction 14-15, 53-97
        extraction rates 61-2
        processing 88-97
        geological aspects 30, 31, 32, 53-4
            Ghana 66-7
    political/social influence 35-6, 44, 185-7
        Ashanti 65, 125-8, 150
    properties/characteristics 30-1, 32-5
        anonymity 123, 130
        chemical inertness (nobility) 30-1, 33, 41, 141
        convertibility 132, 185, 189-92

ductility 33, 34-5
electrical conduction 34, 41
malleability 32-3, 141
melting-point 32, 145
permanence 123, 185
reflectivity 39-41
    safety 132
    softness 32, 36
        hardened 39, 141
    weight 32, 37-9, 53, 55
purity 30-1, 37-8, 146-8
recovery techniques 15, 23-4, 55-62, 68-73, 88-94, 88-90, 91, 93
refining techniques 62-3, 73
sources 31, 32, 53-4, 57-9, 68-9
trading 123-32
value/uses 27-49
    economic 35-7, 123-32, 185-94
    industrial 41
    modern 39-41, 40-1
    ornamental 9, 124, 124, 137-76, 185
    "supernatural" 29-30
    symbolic 9, 122, 123, 124, 132, 137, 150, 185
weighing see weights
see also specific topics
gold beaters' skins 142
gold clay 140-1
Gold Coast 9, 13, 36, 149
    British colonize 11, 12, 15, 65, 66, 170
        Yaa Asantewaa war 13-14, 74
    "European" mining ventures 10-17, 65-7
    European traders in 125-8
    see also Ghana; Ashanti
gold dust 53, 152, 170
    adulterated 173-6
    as currency 9, 29, 123, 158, 171-6, 189
        boxes for 172-3
        "cheating" 173-6
        preparation 172
    as formal gift 186
    powder 140-1, 143
    smuggled 131-2
gold fever 42-8
gold standard 187-92
gold-rushes 44-8, 104-6, 107-8, 189
gold-taker 69
"Golden Age" 30
Golden Axe 158
"Golden Fleece" 185
Golden Rock, Burma 141
Golden Stool 66, 150-1, 157
Golden Temple, Amritsar 124
goldsmiths 167-8
    Ashanti 167-70, 171-2, 177
    crafts 137-77
grains, troy 38
granulation 138-40
grave-robbing 48
Greece, Ancient 101, 123, 138, 185
GSM company 22
Guinea 9, 22
gunpowder 11, 13, 59
guns 128, 156

H

Hadrian, Emperor 102
hallmarking 146-7
hammering see beating
Havana, Cuba 44
Hawaii, Keck Observatory 41
head-bands/hats 28, 140,156-8, 161, 165
headgear (of mines) 14, 78-9

Heap Leach plant 21, 88-9
heat shield 41
helmets 28, 161
Henry VIII, king of England 36
hi-fi equipment 41
Hispaniola 185
hoist gear 10, *78-9*
Homer 129, 141
Hungary 124

I

Iduapriem mine 9, *22*, 88
IFC *see* International Finance Corporation
Imperial College (UK) 25
imperial weight 39
Inca people 29, 42-4, 186
India 23, 123, *124*, 132, 133
industry, gold uses 41
infra-red radiation, reflected 39, 41
ingots 32, 185
    brass 177
    and gold dust 172
    see also bullion
International Finance Corporation (IFC) 19, 21-3
International Monetary Fund 19, 190-2
investment, in gold 194, 195
investment (casting process) 160, 165
iron 32, 138, 168, 185
    hammered 33
Islam/Muslims 124-5, 126, 128
    dinar 124
    Muslims at Obuasi 21
Israel, ancient 141
Italy
    gold coins 124
    gold reserves 192

J

Japan, gold clay 140-1
Jason (and Golden Fleece) 185
jewellery 124, 130, 133, 139
    Ashanti 36, 128, 132, 136, 147
    and smuggling 131
Jimisokakraba 119
Johnson Matthey company 11
Jonah, Samuel Esson (Sam) 18, 19, 24, *25*
Justice's Mine 15, 74

K

karats 37-8, *37*
Keatley, Mark 24
Keck Observatory, Hawaii 41
kenkey 131
kente 158
Klondike, gold-rush 46-8
Kofi Karikari, king of Ashanti 66
'kra discs 165
krennerite 31
Krishna Menon, V.K. 23
Krugerrands (coins) 194
kuduo 125, 126, 172
Kumasi 66, 149, 167-72, 176, 186
Kuntu 13
Kwabrafo stream 119
Kwesi Mensah shaft *78-9*
Kwisa range 10
Kyidom people 145

L

leaching 21, 88-90
    S. America 144-5
    see also Biox
lead, oxidization 32
leaf, gold 34, 141-4
Lindisfarne Gospels 35
lithosphere 53
Load Haul Dump machine 87
long tom 55-6
Lonrho company 18-19, 20, *21*, 23, *25*
lost-wax *see under* casting
Lydia, coins 35, 123, 186

M

MacArthur, John Stewart 62
    MacArthur-Forest Process 62-3
MacCarthy, Sir Charles 150
mace *155*
MacTear, J.A. 14
Madagascar 186
malaria 66, 73
Mali 22, 124, *131*
Mandela, Pres. Nelson 23
manillas 177
Mansa Musa I, king of Mali 124
manuscripts, illuminated 35
Mary, queen of Scots 39
masks 138
mercury 62-3, 90-2, 144
mesh, gold 36
Mesopotamia 138, 186
metals 32, 144-6
    native 30, 53
    oxidization 32
    see also specific metals
Mexico, Spanish conquistadors 42
Midas, king of Phrygia 185
Midras 22
milling 11, 12, 15, 63
mine-workers 98-119
    AGC infrastructure/welfare 20, 72, 115-19
        community projects 116-19
        education 20, 115, 116, 117, 118,119
        health-care 20, 116, 117
        housing 20, 72-3, 114, 116
        recreation/sport 20, 114, 116, 117, 118-19
        relationships 110-11, 115-16, 117, 119
        training 101, 115
    Ashanti deep mines 72, 82, 84-6, 115
    early 101-9, 111-12
    "Free Speak" 116
    migrants 103
        Muslims 21
    numbers at Obuasi 20, 24, 77
        shortage, inter-war 15-16
    porters *see under* transport
    prospectors *see* prospectors
    Quashie era 18
    share-ownership 24
    shift systems 64
    statues of 100, 114
    surveyors 84
    Union 115
    wage-earning, early 104-5, 109, 112
mineralization 76-7
mining
    ancient 100-3, 106
    deep *see* mining: deep
    explosives *see* explosives
    flooding 59

mine design 58-9
open-pit 75, 77, 78, 81, 89
    deforestation 90
    machinery 81
    output 81
    trenches 70
    see also Sansu
regulation of 47
    gold-rushes 107-9
    licences 47
    Rome 102
    S. America 104
    state-ownership 101, 106
    stock-market 47
shallow 10-15, 43, 56, 65
    Ashanti 68-72
    depth of mines 58
    relics dredged 56-7
surface *see* open-pit *above*
treatment processes *see* treatment
mining: deep 57-62, 79, 83-97, 109
    Ashanti 72-3
    cross-section 78-9
    economic aspects 57-8, 61, 109
        extraction rates 61-2
    environmental aspects 63
    lighting 88, 102
    machinery 57, 59-60, 77, 78-9, 81, 83-8
        early, Ghana 71, 73, 74, 112-13
        "river-bed" mimicry 53
    modern workings 74-97
    power supplies 61
        generators 61
    productivity 61-2, 88
    rock-breaking 59-61
        with fire 72
        with water 58
    safety aspects 58, 59-62, 85-6, 101, 115
        Ashanti mines 72
    surveys 77, 80-1
    ventilation/cooling 20, 58, 78-9, 88
    see also Obuasi
Moinsi range 10
money *see* currency
Montezuma II, Aztec king 42
Morocco/Moors 124, 125
Mozambique 22, 23
mpomponsuo 170
Mprakyirie 139

N

Nana Prempeh *see* Prempeh
native metals 30, 53
Netherlands/Dutch, W. African gold 36, 125
New Zealand 56
Newcomen, Thomas 61
Newton, Sir Isaac 188
nickel, alloyed with gold 39
Niger (country) 22
Niger river 125, *131*
nitro-glycerine 59
Nkrumah, Osagyefo/Pres. Dr Kwame 9, 17, 38, *154*
nobles (coins) 124
North Ramp Decline 70
Nseniekye 140
Nuestra Señora de Atocha 128-9
Nuestra Señora de las Marvillas 129
nuggets 31, 32, 52, 53, 54, 152
    and Ashanti status 170, 171

Brazil 48
    and gold dust 171-2
    "largest in the world" 42
Latrobe 32
weathering 52, 54
numismatics 194
Nzema people 112

O

Obuasi: town/district 20, 72-3, 79, 116-19
    District Assembly 117
    European cemetery *17*
    farm 20
    Len Clay Stadium 117
    mosque 21
    see also mine-workers
Obuasi lode/mine 9, 10-25, 63, 68, 71-3, 74, 76-7
    current workings 74-97
        numbers employed 77
        output figures 24, 74-7, 81
    expansion, recent 21-25
        Ashanti Mines Expansion Programme (AMEP) 21-3
        assessment (1990s) 24-5
    imported materials 19-20
    infrastructure 19-20
        see also under transport; mine-workers
    "Obaussie...Estate" 14
    Obuasi shoot 15
    power sources 20
    shallow mines 10-14, 69-70
        Feldtmann report 14
        re-worked 70
        vertical expansion 16
    spoil-heaps/tailings, re-worked 21, 74
Oda river 10
Odumase 119
Offin river 10, *17*, 56
okra 165
okyeame 155-6
open-cast mining *see* mining: open-pit
Opuku Ware I, king of Ashanti 170
Opuku Ware II, Otumfuo, king of Ashanti 150-1, 162-3
Osei Bonsu, king of Ashanti 186
Osei Tutu, king of Ashanti (17 cent.) 150
Osei Tutu Kwame, king of Ashanti (19 cent.) 190
ounces, troy 38-9
oxide ores 21, 81
Oxide Treatment Plant 88, 89
oxidization 32

P

palladium, alloyed with gold 35, 39, 62
Panama 44, 129, 132
panning 54-6, 65, 101
    Ghana 10, 68, 90-2, 111
paper
    and gold leaf 142
    paper money 188-92
Papua New Guinea 185
parchment, and gold leaf 141, 142
pectorals 122, 165
pennyweight 38
Peprah, Richard K. 24
peredwan units 187
Persia, Ancient 35, 123

Peru 42-4, 186
Philip II, king of Macedon 35, 123
pincers, boxwood 142
pipes, tobacco 161
piracy, (16-17 cent.) 44
pit-props 84, 102
Pizarro, Francisco 42
placer deposits 53-7, 101
    Ghana 56, 65, 111
    S. Africa 54-5
    S. America 103-4
platinum, alloyed with gold 35
Pompora processing plant 21, 23, 24, 77, 88-9
portals 70
porters see under transport
Portugal
    S. American gold 103, 104-6
    W. African gold 36, 111, 124-5, 126, 149, 177
        slave-trade 126-7
pound, troy 38-9
Pra river 10, 45, 56, 125
Prempeh I, king of Ashanti 12, 66, 170
pressure hoses 56, 58
prospectors
    gold-rushes 44-8, 107-9
    modern 48-9
pumps 59, 61
punching 137, 156-8

Q
quartering 141-2
quartz, gold-bearing 10, 11, 12, 30, 31, 53-4, 59, 108
Quashie, Lloyd A.K. 18
Queen Mother (Asantehemaa) 153
quills 176
Quimbaya (Colombia) 138, 146

R
Rabbit Creek (Bonanza) 47
raises 58, 81
raising technique 137, 144
Rawlings, Pres. Flt-Lt Jerry John 6-7, 9, 19, 20
red earth 167, 172
reefs 43, 54, 58
refining, off-site 17, 77, 184, 188
religious uses 132, 141, 185, 186
    Ashanti 122, 126, 170
repoussé work 34, 137, 144, 156, 165
riffles, in sifting devices 55-6
Ríotinto mine (Spain) 102
rivers, gold-bearing 31, 45, 46, 54
roasting 15, 20, 89
rock falls 72
rockers/cradles 55-6
rolled/cased gold 146
Rome, Ancient 59, 102
    gold coins 123-4
    gold leaf 141
    mercury extraction process 62
rouge 142
Rowland, R.W. ("Tiny") 18, 19, 23
rubber 128
Russia
    gold leaf 141
    Siberia 101, 106-7
    Trojan gold 129-30

S
Sahara/Sahel 125, 126, 131, 176
salt 125, 126, 185
Saltpond 15
sampling 80-1
San Jago de Cuba 44
sandals 156, 157, 165
Sansu
    electricity 119
    open-pit mine 21, 23, 77, 81
Santa Margarita 128-9
Santarem, Juan de 125
Santo Domingo (Dominican Republic) 44
Sao Paulo di Piratininga (Brazil) 104-6
scales 172, 176
Schliemann, Heinrich 129-30
scribing 137
sea-water, gold in 32
seam see reef
Seko 153
Sekondi 14, 17
Senegal 22, 125
Serra Pellada 48
shafts 57, 58, 61, 69, 71-2, 78-9
    adits 10, 12, 14, 70
    early 101-2, 103-4, 111
    sub-vertical 78-9
Shama 125
sheet, gold 33-4, 141, 144, 152-8, 159, 161, 171
    see also leaf
ships 128-9, 131
Siberia 101, 106-7
Sierra Leone 13
Siguiri mine (Guinea) 9
Sika 'dwa Kofi 150
sika kokoo 29
Sikh religion 124
silver 102, 108, 124, 130
    alloyed with gold 35, 37, 39, 62, 123, 142
        tumbaga 144
    alloyed with mercury 144
    as currency, coins 123, 124
    as currency 186, 188
    gilded 144
    melting-point 32
    mined at Obuasi 77
    reflectivity 39
    S. America 35, 44, 129
    soldering 145
    staff/umbrella finials 152, 155-6
    tarnishing 39
    troy weight 38
skins, gold beaters' 142
slavery 101, 102, 104, 125, 126
    in Americas 104, 129
    among Ashanti 16-17, 111-12, 126, 128, 170, 190
sluices 56, 63
smelting 32, 168
Smith[, C.] & Cade company 11, 15, 17
smuggling 130-2
snake casting 170
soldering 137, 138, 139-40, 144, 162
    rolled gold 146
solidus 123, 124
South Africa 109, 189
    Boer War 12, 13
    Krugerrands 194
    panning 55

reef formation 54
Reserve Bank swap 194
Witwatersrand 54
Soviet Union, former 56
    see also Russia
space technology 40, 41
Spain
    Riotinto mine 102
    S. American gold 35-6, 42-4, 53, 103-4, 144, 185-6
        treasure ships 128-9, 131
    S. American silver 35
Spears, Gen. Sir Edward 17-18, 21
spoil-heaps see tailings
sprue 160-2, 165
Sri Lanka 133
staffs, ceremonial 143, 155-6, 159, 161
stamp mills 11, 15, 105-6
steam power 61
steel 138
    rolled gold 146
Stock Exchanges 18, 24, 195
Stonewall shaft 78-9
stopes 10, 58-9, 78-9, 82
storage tanks 78-9
strikes (gold-bearing levels) 76-7, 83
Sulphide Treatment Plant (Sansu) 64, 88, 90-1, 94-5
    see also Biox
sulphur/sulphide ores 23, 75, 81, 89
Sumer 137
surveyors 84
Sutter's Mill 45
Switzerland
    refining 17, 77, 184, 188
    storage 187-8
swords 148, 150-1, 152, 154, 157, 161, 164-5, 170
sylvanite 31

T
Tailings Treatment Plant 88
tailings/spoil-heaps 21, 58
    re-worked 21, 62, 74, 88, 89-90
talismans 140. 167
Tanzania 22, 88-9
Tarkwa 10, 13, 66, 88
Tekua 164
Tekyiman 170
tellurium/tellurides 31
Thailand 142
Thiobacillus ferro-oxidans 23-4
thread, gold 34-5
tin 32, 61
Tinga 22
Togo 131
touchstones 37, 38, 173
trade 123-32
    "silent" 125
    socio-economic effects 125-8
transport 78-9
    aerial ropeway 16
    porters 12, 14, 16-17, 71, 107, 112-13, 176
    railway access 13, 14, 16-17, 74, 81, 105, 107
    roads 20, 78-9
    tramways/railways, local 14-15, 81
    underground 20, 78-9, 87-8
treasure
    sunken 128-9, 131
    Trojan 129-30

treatment plants 88-94
    final preparation 96-7
trees, gold-bearing 32
    see also deforestation
trenches 70
Troy (Turkey) 129-30
troy weight 38-9
Troyes (France) 39
tumbaga 144-5, 146
Turkey 129-30
    see also Lydia
Turner, G.W. Eaton 16
Tutankhamen, tomb of 30, 31, 34, 141

U
umbrellas 144-5, 152-5, 158-9
United Kingdom see Britain
United States of America 107-8, 190-2
    AGC and 9, 24, 194
    "Air Force One" 41
    California gold-rush 31, 44-6, 55, 56, 107-8, 189
    Fort Knox 190-2
    gold coins 194
    gold devalued 192
    gold reserves 189
    runs on banks 190
    troy weight 39
    see also America: North
Ur, artefacts 137

V
veins, quartz 30, 31
ventilation/cooling systems 20, 58, 78-9, 88, 102
    fires used for 72, 101-2

W
Wangara people 126
water
    for community 119
    for extraction 81, 88
    mine-flooding 59, 102-3
waterwheels 59, 102, 103
Watt, James 61
wax, for cast gold 160-2
weathering 53, 54
weaving 137
weights 32, 37-9, 126, 188
    Ashanti 9, 126, 158, 162, 168, 170, 172, 174-7
Wilson, J.P. 11
Winneba 22
wintzes 58
wire, gold 33, 34-5, 36, 137-8
Witwatersrand 54
World Bank 19
World Health Organization 119
World War I 15, 21, 190
World War II 16-17, 21, 132

Y
Yaa Asantewaa war 13-14, 74
Yukon river/Territory 47-8, 109

Z
Zimbabwe 9, 22, 89
zinc 39, 62-3

ACKNOWLEDGMENTS

Professor Ayensu writes:

It has been my privilege to bring together this commemoration of one of the most important chapters in Ghana's – indeed Africa's – history. The story of Ashanti gold is several thousand years long. The one hundred years that marks Ashanti Goldfields' evolution is surely a remarkable stage in that larger pageant, and the company's pride in its own and the wider story has spurred me on all through this project.

Mr Sam E. Jonah, the Chief Executive, created the opportunity and has been a constant source of inspiration. Mr James K. Anaman, Corporate Affairs Manager, and his staff both in Accra and Obuasi worked closely with me. I am most grateful to the late Mr Nick Laffoley, former Director of AGC Exploration, who provided me with useful archival material and engaged me in innumerable discussions on AGC. Dr John A. Clarke, Director, Mr Adrian de Freitas, Senior Mining Engineer, and Mr Mark Keatley, Chief Financial Officer, gave valuable assistance as the work progressed.

I am especially thankful to Mr and Mrs R.W. "Tiny" Rowland for providing me with photographs and, together with Sir Edward du Cann, KBE, for offering me interesting insights into Lonrho's relations with AGC. I am deeply indebted to Mr T.E. Anin, formerly Chief Executive of the Ghana Commercial Bank and author of *Gold in Ghana*, for offering beneficial information and helping me to appreciate AGC's relationships within the context of the gold industry in Ghana. Mr Maxwell Owusu, former Regional Minister for Ashanti, and Nana Antwi Boasiako, linguist to the Asantehene, Otumfuo Nana Opoku Ware II, helped me to place Ashanti Gold in the context of the Akan culture. Ms Barbara Coleman assisted me with photography and Ms Emma Ampofo offered me superb secretarial and logistical support. Finally, I wish to thank my wife, Dinah, for her understanding and forbearance during my long working hours and travels.

Picture credits

t = top, *b* = bottom, *c* = centre, *l* = left, *r* = right

James K. Anaman 88, 89. Ashanti Goldfields Company 43, 47, 69, 70*l*, 71, 72*l*, 74*b*, 76–77, 103, 105, 106, 107, 108–109, 110–111, 112–113, 118, 119, 195. Edward S. Ayensu 10, 12, 14*b*, 24*t*, 25, 36*tl*, *bl*, 38*tr*, *br*, 49, 52, 55, 56, 63, 70*r*, 72*r*, 73, 74*t*, 80, 84, 91*tr*, 92, 96, 97, 100, 102, 104, 114, 115, 116*t*, *b*, 118, 126*tr*, 127, 128*b*, 132, 139, 140, 143, 145, 147*t*, 150, 151, 153, 154, 155, 156*tr*, *b*, 157, 158, 159*b*, 160, 162, 163, 164*bl*, *br*, 165*bl*, *br*, 177, 182, 188*t*. Stephen Barnett 26–27, 50–51, 58, 60, 61, 62, 64, 75, 76*b*, 81, 82, 83, 85, 86, 87, 88, 89*l*, 90, 91*c*, 94, 95, 96, 116*t*, 172, 173, 174, 175, 182–183, 186. Bridgeman Art Library 34*r*, 38*l* and *c*, 138*t*. British Museum 120–121, 122, 125, 134–135, 136, 146, 148, 156 *tl*, 161, 162*t*, 164*t*, 165*t*, 166, 167, 168, 169, 170, 171. Christie's Images 129. Peter Clayton 30*r*, 35*r*, 131, 146*tl*. E.T. Archive 42, 46, 138*b*, Werner Forman Archive 126*t*, *l* and *b*. Robert Harding Picture Library 37*t*. Michael Holford 28, 34*l*, 35*l*, 176. Paul List 74*b*. London Assay Office / P.V.A. Johnson 37*b*. Magnum/Erich Hartmann 187. Natural History Museum 30*l*, 31, 32*r*. Panos Pictures 141, 142. N.M. Rothschild & Sons Ltd 190, 192. Science Photo Library 32*l*, 33, 40, 54. TRIP 124. World Gold Council 39. Worshipful Company of Goldsmiths ZEFA 36*r*, 41, 48, 80*cr*, 133, 184, 188*b*, 193. *If the publishers have unwittingly infringed copyright in any illustration reproduced, they would pay an appropriate fee on being satisfied to the owner's title.*

The publisher would like to thank Mining Magazine for use of their archive material.